GREENWOOD SUMMER

To TED,

with love

Greenwood Summer

by Marjory Bartlett Sanger

Illustrated by Christine Price

E. P. Dutton Co., Inc., New York, 1958

652490

LIBRARY OF CONGRESS CATALOG CARD NUMBER: 58-9572

ACKNOWLEDGMENT

*While the characters and setting of GREENWOOD
SUMMER are fictitious, the inspiration for Camp
Greenwood was drawn from the Massachusetts Audubon
Society's Wildwood Nature Camp, directed by David R.
Miner.*

CONTENTS

CHAPTER ONE

A CHRISTMAS PRESENT IN JULY

Cousin Laura was famous for her Christmas presents. At least, that's what Brian and Jenny Vogel said. Two years ago she had sent a hickory-smoked ham from her farm in Maryland. And last year she had given them a bird feeder.

Before the arrival of the feeder, Brian and Jenny had not been particularly interested in birds. And they hadn't known much about them. Oh, they knew blue jays and crows, of course, and robins. But they had believed that all sparrows were the same, and they had never thought of a flicker being a woodpecker.

Cousin Laura's present had changed that. When the birds started coming to the feeder for seed, the children watched them and looked them up in a book, and later they went on bird walks and made explorations of their own. Brian had kept a list of all the birds he identified; it had once been his ambition to see a hundred different kinds.

But now, instead of trying to add as many names as possible to his list, he wanted to learn about the birds themselves, their habits and behavior, their ways of living in their environments. He had thought of choosing one species and studying all he could about it, but it was so hard to decide which to choose. Eagles had always been his favorites, but eagles were not easy to find. He had seen only a couple in his life, and those had been together, and on a special field trip with leaders who knew where eagles were.

Jenny, Brian's younger sister, liked the merry goldfinch that bounded through the summer air in black and yellow, calling, "Potato chip," as it dipped in flight. In winter it wore a dull dress of olive green. The children discovered that when one alighted on the white pine they had trimmed yes-

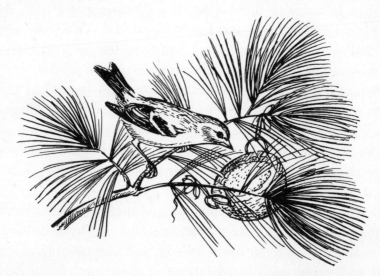

terday, Christmas Eve, outside the kitchen window. It was a birds' Christmas Tree, decorated with cranberry and popcorn strings, stale doughnuts, and orange halves filled with chickadee pudding, made of peanut butter, suet, and seeds. And the birds flocked around it.

To his great joy, Brian had received binoculars as his gift from his parents. He was almost thirteen and old enough for a pair, they said, and besides it was all he had asked for. He had thought of nothing else since looking through Cousin Laura's at the plovers and sandpipers on a Cape Cod beach last August. This very moment he was out in the field beyond the road, scanning the edge of the woods.

"The days will begin to get longer now," Mrs. Vogel observed, and that, thought Jenny, was the best Christmas present of all.

"Brian, come back," his father called to him. "We're not through opening packages." If they hadn't been so interested in birds they would have finished hours ago. Other years it had not taken half so long.

"*I'm* through," answered Brian, and he meant it. His binoculars were all he cared about now.

"There's still Cousin Laura's left," Jenny pointed out.

"You can have that one," her brother told her, busy focusing on some juncos and tree sparrows in a weedy thicket.

"That's what you said last year," Mrs. Vogel reminded him. "And look what it turned out to be."

The feeder, thought Jenny. It had started everything. "Let's see what Cousin Laura's giving us this time."

The package was so thin and flat that it might have been an envelope. Indeed, thought Brian, it probably was. "Money?" he suggested hopefully.

"I don't think," his mother said, "she'd be giving you money."

9

"What's wrong with that?" Brian wanted to know. He had seen his father preparing those narrow red envelopes for the postman and the milkman.

"There's nothing *wrong* with it," his mother explained; "it's just that it wouldn't be like Cousin Laura."

Jenny had been untying the ribbon carefully and slowly. She did this to save it, and also to prolong the suspense of opening. "But it's only a Christmas card," she said at last. She shook her head. This wasn't like Cousin Laura either.

"A Christmas card wouldn't be wrapped up," Brian objected.

Wordlessly she held it out to him. On the cover was a wreath with birds perched like ornaments around it, and the verse:

"I heard a bird sing in the dark of December,
 'We are nearer to Spring than we were in September.'"

That's pretty, Jenny thought, and the idea pleased her. She liked spring best because it was then that the birds, in their most colorful plumage, sang so constantly and clear. Cousin Laura knew that; she must have remembered it when she selected the card. Still, Jenny thought sadly, it wasn't the same as a present. She realized that she was more disappointed than she should have been. Christmas, her mother had often told them, was a time to think of giving, not receiving. That was the Christmas spirit. Yet there must be some reason for Cousin Laura's doing this. Perhaps she had been too concerned with presents for her own children this year. Jenny could picture Jill and Toby in that big hall

with the Audubon prints, and a tremendous tree that rose
up through the center of the curving stairs with a great pile
of boxes underneath. Musing about this, she looked back at
the card.

"Well, open it," Brian was saying with his customary im-
patience.

Inside Cousin Laura had written a message in green ink.
"Your present this year will come in July."

"July!" both children cried. Nothing seemed farther away.
Why, spring will have come and gone by then, thought
Jenny, awed. "What can it be?" she wondered.

"Firecrackers," guessed Brian. But that, also, didn't sound
like Cousin Laura.

"Maybe a puppy," their mother was suggesting, "a puppy
that isn't ready to travel yet."

"We already have Brillig," said Jenny. "I wouldn't want
another dog. Neither would Brillig." Brillig was a German
shepherd, and a member of the family.

"A cat, then," said Mr. Vogel, teasing.

"Laura wouldn't be apt to send a feeding station one year
and a cat the next," his wife pointed out.

"The bird feeder would become a cat feeder," Brian declared with a big smile. He was happy with his binoculars; it didn't matter to him that Cousin Laura's present was delayed. When July came he would have forgotten about it anyway. "She could get by this time," he remarked, "with not sending anything at all."

But Cousin Laura, Jenny knew, did not try to "get by" with things. If she said something would come in July, it surely would, and seem all the better for the waiting. Jenny was ten, and beginning to realize things like this. Still, summer was a long way off. "Do *you* know what Cousin Laura's present is?" she asked her mother.

"I haven't the slightest idea," Mrs. Vogel asserted. "It's a complete mystery." And Jenny, who was wise about her parents, knew she could believe her.

But in a few days the mystery was solved. A large envelope addressed to both children came in the mail. And inside was a folder with the words *Greenwood Nature Camp* printed across the cover in letters that looked as if they had been made of little logs. Inside of *that* were photographs and maps and paragraphs of printing, and around the month of July a circle had been drawn. Brian and Jenny understood in a flash what this meant. It seemed to take their parents a little longer to comprehend the full significance. The children had noticed that this was sometimes true of grownups.

"Well!" Mr. and Mrs. Vogel exclaimed at last. "So that's your Christmas present from Cousin Laura. Greenwood Nature Camp. Doesn't it sound wonderful?"

After he had recovered from the first moment of surprise, Brian was not sure whether he thought it sounded wonderful or not. He had never been away to camp. Summer was always his free time, and he looked forward to it for that very reason. Last July he had been so content just walking in the woods looking for birds. After the restrictions of school the rest of the year he was not certain that he wanted to give up this summertime freedom. "Nature doesn't necessarily mean birds," he began doubtfully. "It can be lots of other things." He had learned this in science class. And he wasn't interested in anything but birds just now, especially since he had his binoculars. "Butterflies and flowers are all right for girls."

"What about snakes?" his mother asked. "You like *them,* don't you?"

"I can find snakes by myself, around the pond. And frogs and turtles too, if I want to." It was true, he was good at finding things like these. "I don't have to go to camp to see them."

Jenny was listening to this conversation with apprehension. Her mother, watching her, realized that it had been a mistake to mention snakes. "There probably won't be any

13

there anyway," she said hastily, but Jenny stored up in her mind all she had heard.

"It won't be just about birds," maintained Brian, going back to his first objection.

"Well, of course not," his father told him. "How could you spend a month on nothing but birds?"

A month? thought Brian. He was planning to devote his entire life to studying birds. He had even announced once that he was going to be an ornithologist, though he had not yet said this to his family.

A startling thought occurred to Jenny. "Will Toby and Jill be there too?" she asked.

"Why, I should think so," her mother replied. "I can't imagine Cousin Laura sending you two and not her own children."

"That settles it then," said Brian, as though every angle had been weighed and considered. "I couldn't stand to be with Toby for a whole month."

It was what Jenny had been privately thinking about Jill. And it was too bad, she thought wistfully. A camp like Greenwood, under the right conditions, might be a lot of fun.

"You're with Toby and Jill for two weeks every August at the Cape," her parents were telling Brian.

"But that's different," Brian protested. "At the Cape you and Cousin Laura are there. This way I'd have to be alone with him."

"The folder says the camp takes fifty boys and girls. That doesn't sound as if you'd be very much *alone* with *anybody*."

Brian sat contemplating his fate with a quiet resignation. All of his objections had been met and answered. As usual his parents had been able to point him in the direction they wanted. It was remarkable and discouraging the way they always managed it. "Do I have to go?" he asked at last.

Yes, wondered his sister, do we have to go?

Their parents exchanged a glance. "We'll see," Mrs. Vogel said. "We needn't settle it today."

Jenny sighed. It was the same with so many things. She would like to be certain then and there what she would be doing in July, just as she always wanted to know ahead of time what she would be having for supper. She had once heard a grownup say that children were lucky because they didn't have to make major decisions. It would be better, she sometimes felt, if grownups would make a few more.

Brian picked up his binoculars and went out into the wintry day. At the sight of him, chickadees that seemed to know him, perhaps because he fed them, flocked around. I don't *have* to go to this nature camp, he told himself. Be-

tween now and July I'll be able to think of a way out. And he raised his glasses to see if the birds that had been there at Christmas were still feeding in the weed patch.

"Aren't young people astonishing?" Mrs. Vogel said to her husband. "As well as I know ours, I never cease to be amazed by them. Wouldn't you have thought they'd be thrilled to go to a place like Greenwood?"

"Yes," her husband agreed, "I would indeed."

"I made a mistake when I mentioned snakes. I realized it as soon as I said it."

"Yet," pointed out Mr. Vogel, "the real objection seemed to be Toby and Jill. What is it our children have against them? They always seem friendly enough when they're together."

"I think it's just that they haven't much in common. You know how annoyed Brian gets with Toby's constant talk of baseball. And Jill is absorbed now with movies and movie stars. They don't seem to care for the out-of-doors in spite of the fact that they live on a farm."

"Then why does Laura choose a nature camp?"

"Oh, in the hope of stirring up some interest, I suppose. She loves it all so much. But it does seem too bad; they

16

surely won't enjoy it. And Brian and Jenny would evidently be much happier there without them."

Mr. Vogel shook his head. "It's very good of Laura," he said, "to want to send our young ones. Do you think we should let her do it?"

"I wondered too," his wife told him, "until I realized it may be the only way she can persuade her own. Ironically, Jill and Toby probably wouldn't be happy at camp if Brian and Jenny *weren't* with them."

"So," concluded Mr. Vogel, "if our children don't go, Laura's won't either."

"Well, of course, that's only a guess of mine," Mrs. Vogel replied, "but I believe it's true." She looked out across the field to where Jenny had now joined her brother. "And I also believe," she went on, "that when the time comes, Brian and Jenny will be anxious to go. But," she added, smiling, "that's only a guess too."

CHAPTER TWO

DECISIONS AND A
WOODCOCK'S SONG

IN LATE March, even in New England, come days almost warm enough to set one dreaming of summer. Birds return and search out nesting territories, leaf buds begin to lose their tightness, an early bee drones by, and flocks of midges rise in the air.

"Brian," asked his sister, "have you been thinking about Greenwood Nature Camp?"

"No," Brian answered casually, "not much." Actually he had thought about it a great deal, but without any pleasure. His chief concern was still to find some excuse for not having to go. But so far he hadn't been able to think of a good enough reason.

The children and Brillig had walked down to a neighboring pond, coming by way of the damp woods in the hope of hearing fox sparrows sing. But except for a pair of golden-crowned kinglets squeaking through the branches, and a hairy woodpecker examining a dead tree, the woods had been very quiet.

At the pond, however, a red-winged blackbird was calling, perched on a cattail, hunching up, and spreading its wings to show its brilliant shoulder patches. A song sparrow caroled in an alder thicket. Willows bent tendrils like yellow hair to the brook's edge. And on the brown surface close to shore a few water striders moved about, slowly, as if testing the warmth of the sun.

"Do you think we'll be going?" Jenny asked. She would like to have it settled now, definitely, one way or the other.

Brian frowned at the bright water as though displeased by it. "I haven't been able to think of a way *not* to go," he said. "But something's bound to occur to me before long."

Jenny admired her brother very much. If he said he'd think of something, he surely would. And if he felt it was better to be free in the summertime and not go to camp, then that must be true too.

Brillig had chased a woodchuck into a stone wall, and stood now on top of a rock, sniffing and barking. The song sparrow stopped singing as if to listen, and the red-wing rose from its cattail, and with a gurgling "Conk-la-ree" sailed to the other end of the pond where the first tree swallows were skimming.

"Mr. Crandall," Brian said to his science teacher with a seriousness that commanded all of Mr. Crandall's attention, "would you go to camp if you could stay home instead and be out in the woods and fields?"

Mr. Crandall considered this. "That would depend, I should say, on the kind of camp it was."

Brian was a little disconcerted. He had hoped for a positive and unqualified "No" which would put an end to the question forever. "A nature camp," he murmured reluctantly, fearing that this would sway Mr. Crandall in its favor.

And he was right. His teacher's face brightened. "If it were a camp like Greenwood, I'd say to jump at the chance. As a matter of fact, I was going to suggest it to you. I'd even recommend you for a scholarship. If it were a nature camp like Greenwood, you couldn't do better than to go."

"It *is* Greenwood," Brian said slowly. He felt as though he had been caught in a sort of trap. Now, glad or sorry, he sensed he had no further choice in the matter. "I won't need a scholarship," he added. "Cousin Laura's sending me."

"Well, you're a lucky boy, Brian. And I'm sure you'll gain a great deal from it. Who knows, perhaps you'll be able to contribute something too."

A thought occurred to Brian. "Did *you* go to Greenwood?" he asked.

Mr. Crandall shook his head. "But I would have tried to if there'd been such a place when I was growing up."

As Brian walked away, absorbed with what now seemed his destiny, one more objection came to him. "Girls go too," he puffed, hurrying back to where his teacher stood watching him dreamily and smiling, "and there may be sissy subjects like butterflies and wildflowers."

Mr. Crandall still smiled. "Do you think it's sissy to fly from Canada to the Gulf of Mexico?" he asked. "That's what one kind of butterfly does. And do you think it's sissy to hitchhike halfway across the country on the backs of animals and in freight cars? That's what the seeds of some wildflowers do. Keep an open mind, Brian; everything in nature has its value and fascination. You just have to *know* about it. Don't ever, all your life, turn down an opportunity to learn."

That very same day Jenny received a letter. And it was from someone she had never even heard of. Baby raccoons played around the border of the paper. And the letter said:

"Dear Jenny:

I have just found out that you may be coming to Greenwood this summer, and I want to tell you how glad I am. I've been at Greenwood for several years now, and each time I love it more. It's a wonderful place. There's so much

21

to do and discover. You're going to love it too, I know. I'll be anxious to meet you in July, so be sure to come, won't you?

Your new friend,
Rosalie Sears"

"But," asked Jenny, "how did she know about me?"

"The letter comes from Maryland," her mother pointed out. "She must be a friend of Jill's."

She doesn't sound much like Jill, thought Jenny. Anyway, she's *my* friend now, she said so; my new friend.

She read the letter several times over, and then put it carefully away in her handkerchief box. She couldn't answer it because there was no return address. She would have to deliver the message in person in July.

Mr. Crandall had a surprise for Brian and Jenny. But he wouldn't tell them what it was. They only knew they were to meet him in the schoolyard just after sunset.

"Won't it be getting too dark for a bird walk then?" Mr. Vogel remarked, more than ever convinced that bird watchers chose the most astounding times of day for their excursions.

"What can it be?" Jenny asked Brian. It sometimes seemed that her life was full of surprises. Her brother, she noticed, had been strange and preoccupied recently. She wondered what he could have on his mind. If he was moody it would be even more difficult to tell him that she had decided to go to Camp Greenwood.

At the schoolyard Mr. Crandall was waiting for them in his car. Still with no word of explanation he drove them out beyond the last houses on the edge of town. The sunset light had all but died from the sky, and the air was a vibrant blue-green. The birch trees, not yet fully leafed, stood ghostlike and pale. "I didn't want to say anything about this," their teacher told them, "for fear it mightn't happen, and you'd be disappointed. But it's all right; I hear it now."

Brian and Jenny, who had been alert and listening, had heard not a sound. "Come quietly," Mr. Crandall said, and they left the car and walked like shadows to a field where they waited beside a cedar. Then, "Peent, peent," came through the dusky stillness.

"A nighthawk," whispered Brian, who had heard similar calls from Boston roof tops on summer evenings in the city.

"No," replied Mr. Crandall, "this is not a nighthawk. What you are about to hear is the flight song of the woodcock."

"I thought woodcocks were game birds," said Brian. "I didn't know they sang."

"They don't sing in the way that we think of songbirds singing. But in the spring, at dusk or sometimes in the moonlight, the male will rise into the air and make a series of sounds that we call a song. Listen."

"Peent, peent, peent," came from the bird on the ground. Then all at once it rose, its long bill plainly silhouetted against the sky, and, making a whistling noise with its wings, climbed in wide arcs, going round and round in an upward and finally narrowing spiral. They could just make out its dark shape ascending. At the top of its flight it seemed to tumble and roll fluttering down and around with a rapid series of warbles, bleats, and cries. Then like a falling ball it dropped quite silently to earth. And, "Peent, peent," came once more from the darkening field.

The children were transfixed. "Why does it do that?" Brian wanted to know.

"For the reason," Mr. Crandall told him, "that a grouse drums and a crane dances. To attract a mate."

"Will it do it again?" asked Jenny, hoping.

As if in answer, the woodcock soared into the air and repeated its remarkable performance. And this time when it

dropped to the ground it landed not fifteen feet from where they stood. Entranced, they watched it parade swiftly about, pointing its bill, and calling. When its head was turned toward them, the sound seemed very close, as indeed it was, and when it was turned in the opposite direction, it sounded halfway across the field.

Brian was asking his teacher a great many questions about how air and feathers can create whistling effects, but Jenny hardly listened to their conversation. She felt that there was something mystical about this flight and song, the way there was about the ceremonies of Indian tribes and the rites of the Druids, and she did not wish to have all the mysteries explained to her.

"Jenny," said Brian abruptly, after Mr. Crandall had taken them home, "I have something to tell you. I've decided to go to Greenwood Nature Camp after all." He said this very fast, as though anxious to have it over with, and then sighed in relief.

And, "Oh, Brian," said Jenny, also in relief, "I was just about to tell *you* the same thing."

It was planned that Toby and Jill would spend the night before camp with the Vogels. Mr. Vogel would drive them all up to Greenwood the next day. Brian and Jenny groaned, but Mrs. Vogel said, "Considering Cousin Laura's sending you, the least we can do is invite her children here. You wouldn't want them to spend the night in a hotel, would you?"

From the grown-up look of Jill, thought Jenny, she would probably have preferred the hotel. Although only just thirteen, she wore high heels and lipstick, and seemed dressed for anything but a nature camp. Jenny had not seen her since last August on the Cape, and she marveled at the change in her. And from the way her mother looked at her, she could tell that she was surprised too.

"You look like a movie star," Jenny said, knowing this would please her.

"Yes," agreed Jill, "I do, don't I?"

"Are you looking forward to camp?"

"Heavens, no! Are you?"

Jenny thought of asking about Rosalie Sears; then she decided not to. She would continue to keep her new friend a secret. But, she thought, appalled, suppose she turns out to be like Jill? Suppose *all* the girls there are like Jill?

Toby, a year younger than his sister, had brought his baseball bat. It was the first thing Brian saw when he walked in the door. "There's no baseball at Greenwood," he told him. "It said in the folder, 'No sports.'"

"I know," replied Toby gloomily, and his face asked, What kind of a camp can that be? "But I thought I'd bring my bat along so I could swing it now and then and not forget completely what it feels like. I don't suppose you've been to many big league games this year," he added, still gloomy.

"I haven't been to *any*," Brian told him honestly. "I got a pair of binoculars for Christmas, and I've been pretty busy looking through them."

"Looking at what?"

"Birds mostly. And, and other things," he went on, remembering that Toby didn't think much of birds. "Are you glad you're going to Greenwood?"

"Of course not. What about you?"

It was, thought Brian, Toby's mother who was sending them. He had better be polite. "It may not be so bad," he said.

CHAPTER THREE

CHANGING FEELINGS

A SCROLL-SHAPED sign proclaimed *Greenwood Forest,* and hanging below it was a log with the letters that spelled *Greenwood Nature Camp.* Brian let out his breath slowly. Far in the back of his mind had been the possibility that there might really be no such place, that the whole thing was a myth or fairy tale. Now here they were.

"Isn't it beautiful!" said Mrs. Vogel appreciatively.

"The camp must be right in the forest," Mr. Vogel told them.

"No wonder there's no baseball," said Brian.

"But there's everything else," breathed Jenny.

Toby and Jill sat without a word.

Down a winding woodland trail they went, under oaks and white pines where thrushes were singing and other birds

28

moved through the shadowy denseness of the branches. Here and there a deep-orange lily opened like a flaming star. Yellow and black butterflies, tiger swallowtails, followed the opening the road made through the trees. Jenny saw a nest with paper straws woven into it. And her brother heard a call he had never heard before. It was vireo-like and unhurried. "Stop a minute, Dad," he cried, "that's a new bird!"

But other cars were coming along behind them, bringing more campers to Greenwood. "I can't stop now," his father said. "You'll have a whole month to look for new birds."

It will go very fast, thought Brian, and then smiled, realizing what this thought must mean, an indication of his changing feelings about camp.

29

They came at last to a clearing and a cabin at the edge of a pond. On all sides towered the pines, reflected in the still water. The cabin had a wide porch around it, and over the door was the one word *Greenwood*.

"Do we all sleep in *there?*" asked Toby, breaking his long silence.

"Of course not, silly," said his sister. "We sleep in tents. Rosalie told us that."

So, thought Jenny, Rosalie *was* a friend of Jill's. She might have known—indeed she had guessed—yet she had been so anxious for Rosalie to be *her* friend. She had thought about her all the way to camp.

A tall blond man was coming out of the cabin. He jogged down the steps of the porch and over to the car. "Hello," he said; "my name's Dillon. Are these new campers?" And he included them all in his smile.

"Four of them for you," Mr. Vogel reported, holding out his hand. "We're the Vogels and the Ashtons," and he indicated which was which. He remembered seeing in the folder that Mr. Dillon was the camp director. "What would you like me to do with them?"

For a moment Jenny feared that her father was about to let them out then and there, and drive off at once: She looked at Jill and was surprised to see that she too seemed worried. She was very quiet and her mouth, even under the pink lipstick, had an anxious expression.

Mr. Dillon was consulting a list. "Toby Ashton and Brian Vogel are in the same tent, Spotted Salamander. Jill Ashton is in Purple Finch, and Jenny Vogel is in Partridgeberry. Our tents are all named for wild things here in the forest." And he handed them a map with the locations marked in red pencil, and told Mr. Vogel he could drive on the trails to reach the tents and unload the children's baggage. "We don't usually allow cars down there," he added, "but today's a little different." And with a quick wave he was off to greet another family.

"What a nice man," Mrs. Vogel said, with satisfaction. Jenny had never been away from home without her before, and her mother had been wondering how she would make out. Now she felt certain all would go well.

Jenny was thinking, I don't have to be with Jill. But no sooner had this been settled than she had a slight twinge of concern. They would all be strangers, except for Rosalie, who would surely be in her tent since she had taken the trouble to write. Purple Finch sounded nicer than Partridgeberry, she thought, but maybe that was because it was such a beautiful bird, colored the purple of ancient times, as Mr. Crandall had told them. One had come to their feeder last winter. Anyway she was glad that Toby hadn't seen the look Brian had sent to the back seat when Mr. Dillon said that he and Toby would be together.

I *knew* I'd end up with him, Brian told himself rebelliously. But the tent was a large one with four double-decker bunks. Toby's was at one end, and Brian's the other. From the tent platform he could look right out into the woods. I'll be able to see birds without even raising my head, he thought. "You can go birding from your pillow," his father said.

"Are birds your special interest?" asked the counselor in charge. He was slender and dark and looked as if he might be in his first year of college.

31

"Yes. Are they yours?"

"Well, I like them. I don't know too much about them. I guess reptiles and amphibians are what I like most. How about you?" and he turned to include Toby in the conversation.

Brian could have guessed his answer. "Baseball," said Toby.

The counselor smiled. "You won't get that around here, I'm afraid. But there'll be lots else to keep you busy. By the way, I'm Dan Alderman. I asked for this tent because of its name. I think we'll have a pretty good group."

Except for one, thought Brian. "Can you imagine," he muttered disgustedly to his father, "saying *baseball* when he was asked that question?"

"Shhh," warned his father. "Knowing Toby, I can imagine it quite easily." He helped his son sort out the rest of his belongings—field guides, notebooks, boots, and poncho. Brian had his binoculars around his neck.

"Did you hear Dan say he didn't know much about birds? I sure hope someone around here does. Why do you suppose they'd have a counselor who doesn't know about birds?"

"Because," Mr. Vogel told him patiently, "he probably knows a great deal about reptiles. Everybody can't know about everything. Perhaps you can teach him something. Wouldn't you enjoy that?"

"What's a spotted salamander?" asked Jenny. She wondered if it was anything like a spotted sandpiper.

"It's an amphibian," said her brother. "That means it lives part of its life in water and part on land. But don't ask me what one looks like, because I haven't the slightest idea."

There must be salamanders here, he thought, because Mr. Dillon had said the tents were named for things in the forest. And Brian started casting his eyes about on the smooth thick carpet of pine needles.

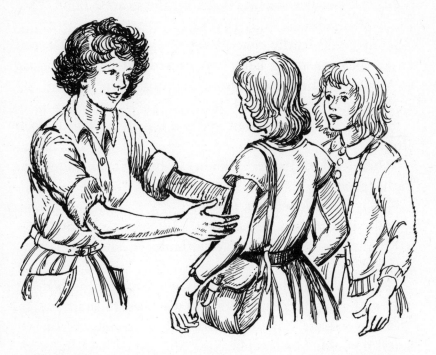

At the tent called Purple Finch a pretty girl bounded out and met Jill with a hug. Jenny did not have to be told that this was Rosalie Sears. And she was a counselor! Jenny couldn't have been more amazed. "I had no idea you were a counselor," she said when Jill introduced them.

"I was a camper first," Rosalie said easily. "I was a camper here for three years. It was wonderful. I really envy you."

"Isn't it wonderful to be a counselor?" Jenny asked.

"Oh, yes. But it's different. You have to think about the campers a lot, all the time, in fact, if you're a *good* counselor. When you're a camper you can, well, just enjoy things more. I know you'll enjoy every minute of Greenwood."

Jill had put her suitcase down on the nearest bunk. "No, Jill," called Rosalie, "this is yours, over near me."

Jenny could hardly conceal her disappointment. "Do you mean you're sleeping here?" she asked Rosalie.

"Why, yes, I've always been in Purple Finch."

"I thought you'd be with me."

"Well, I wish I were, but you see this is my tent to look after."

"Then," asked Jenny, "couldn't I be here instead of in Partridgeberry?"

"Jenny," cautioned her mother.

"This bed has my name on it!" Jill was exclaiming.

Rosalie laughed. "Didn't you think we knew you were coming?"

"But in a hotel they don't put your name on the bed."

Even Jenny, disconsolate as she was, had to smile at this.

"My goodness," Rosalie protested, "Greenwood isn't a hotel! It couldn't be less like one." She turned back to Jenny. "Partridgeberry is a lovely tent. In some ways it's the nicest of all. It has a beautiful view of the pond down through the trees."

Jill looked interested. "Is it a nicer tent than this?" she asked.

"Oh, I'll trade places with you," Jenny said quickly, seeing what was in her mind.

"No, I guess not," Jill decided. "After all, I can see water

34

whenever I want to at home. We live on a river, you know," she added to Rosalie, and there was something wistful about her expression then. She must be missing it, Jenny thought, suddenly sorry for her.

Partridgeberry was, as Rosalie had said, a lovely tent. It was of pale-green canvas with only three bunks in it. Jenny found the one with her name on it, and from there she could see the glistening water of the pond. A bush, covered with white flowers, grew nearby. Soft-looking ferns raised their delicate fronds. Wood thrushes sang all around, and not far away an ovenbird was calling. The forest resounded with its "Teacher, teacher, teacher."

"You're going to love it here," Mrs. Vogel said as they left Jenny unpacking and placing her things in an orderly arrangement on the shelves of the orange crate by her bed.

And, "Yes," agreed Jenny thankfully, "I'm sure I am."

Toby picked up his bat and started swinging it. He took enormous cuts at imaginary pitches. "What's that for?" asked Dan Alderman, the counselor.

"To hit balls with," said Toby. "In a game called baseball."

Dan reached out and took the bat, but he didn't swing it. "I play baseball too," he said evenly, "but not here. This is a nature camp. So I think I'll just keep this for you in my foot locker. That way it won't get lost, and it can't hurt anybody."

"Hurt anybody?" echoed Toby, incredulous.

"All sorts of things can happen, and probably will, before the summer's over. But there's no sense in taking unnecessary chances. I usually end up with quite a collection of sheath knives, but this is the first baseball bat I've ever confiscated."

"What's so bad about a sheath knife?" Brian wanted to know.

"Not a thing, if it's properly handled. But with a big group of boys it's hard to tell who knows how to use one and who doesn't. By the time you find out, someone may have lost a toe. So—no sheath knives. You can do all the cutting and whittling you'll need to do here with a jackknife."

Brian had finished his unpacking. Under Dan's supervision everything was neatly put away. "But *keeping* it neat's another story," Dan said, shaking his head as though from long experience. "We have inspection every day. It's up to me to see that Salamander gets the best marks."

"Inspection, just like the army," grumbled Toby.

"Yes," agreed Dan, "good training for you."

"Is there anyone here," Brian asked quickly, "who *does* know a lot about birds?"

"Mr. Dillon's the bird man. He's supposed to be really good."

"Does he take people on walks? Me, for instance?"

Dan nodded, and Brian bounded up at once with his binoculars. "But not *today*," Dan went on hastily. "This is registration day. Tomorrow's when camp actually starts. Then everything will begin to happen."

And Brian, who had been so reluctant to come to camp, thought he could hardly wait until tomorrow.

CHAPTER FOUR

THE HIGH NOON OF THE YEAR

THE RISING sun, shining between the tree trunks of Green-wood Forest, awakened Jenny. The woods were filled with such a radiance that every fern and twig and flower seemed aglow. Each pine needle too was touched with brilliance as the light fell in long aisles between the trees.

The others in her tent were sound asleep. They must be used to sleeping out-of-doors. But down by the pond a boy with binoculars was walking. Recognizing her brother, Jenny dressed quickly and slipped out to join him.

"Did the sun wake you up?" she asked.

"The sun? Gosh, no. I was awake before the sun. It was the birds. Didn't you hear them?"

"Which birds?"

"All of them, and all singing at once. Mostly thrushes, but there were robins and towhees and some warblers I didn't

38

know. I couldn't find the one I heard yesterday, the one that sounded like a vireo. It must stay back where the leafy woods mix in with the evergreens."

He did not, thought his sister, seem as disappointed as he would have the year before if he had failed to add a new bird to his list.

"Jenny, what do you think? There's a blind boy in our tent."

She was astonished by this piece of news, as he had known she would be. "But why would he want to come to Greenwood? I mean, what could he get out of nature?"

Brian shook his head. "He knows a lot about it though," he said. "He and Dan were talking about salamanders, and he described one to me perfectly, just as if he'd actually seen it. His name's David Blair, and he has the bunk next to mine."

"Ee-o-lay," sang the wood thrushes, starting up a second chorus. And that at least, thought Jenny gratefully, was one thing that a blind boy could enjoy.

They all met in the workshop after breakfast. This was a big room in the main cabin, and was fitted out with shelves and tables and chairs. At one end was a library. Around the walls were exhibits—mounted birds and butterflies, a wild-flower chart, a map of the summer skies, an ant farm, and a cross-section of a beehive with live bees coming and going through a little runway. There was also a model of a beaver house and dam, crowded in with other displays. It's like a museum, Brian thought. "And you'll add to it," Dan Alderman told him. "The campers make their own exhibits too."

Mr. Dillon, the director, was calling them together at the library end of the room. Jenny had not seen him since the night before at the opening service when he had lighted their candles. It was a beautiful and impressive ceremony. The campers had formed a circle in the darkened dining hall, and each was given an unlit candle to hold. Then Mr. Dillon went around the circle lighting all the candles from the flame of one he carried. And to every boy and girl he spoke a separate word of welcome. As their candles were lit the campers who knew the words began singing a song called "Witchcraft," until the whole dining hall was filled with the sound of their voices, and the candles made a complete ring of light. Then Mr. Dillon told them that this ring was a symbol of God's love which at all times surrounded them and was visible wherever they looked for it in the world of nature.

Now in the workshop he stood before them, already a familiar and popular figure. Jenny felt somehow more at ease when he was around. She said this to Jill, who came to sit beside her, and Jill nodded. She was, Jenny noticed, wearing simple camp clothes, and had left off her lipstick.

"Most of you," Mr. Dillon began, "have come to Greenwood to learn more about nature. Not just one phase, or two

40

or three phases, but many phases. And, most important, to learn how these phases are related, one to another, as, for example, Brian Vogel is related to his sister Jenny, and also, though in a different way, to his cousin Toby Ashton. It's a big subject."

Brian felt pleased to have been singled out like this, and his new friend David Blair, sitting on his left, smiled at him.

"The study of this interrelationship, or interdependence, is called 'ecology.' Now you are not college students, or even high school students, so we're not going to confuse you with a string of long words and strange terms. I only want you to understand this: In nature nothing stands alone. Physical surroundings, climate, and time all act together to create, establish, and then alter. For nothing stays still. Mountains are changing, rivers are changing, the forest around us, and the ponds are changing. Watch the changes and you can read the story of the earth in them."

Jenny heard a steady click, click, click behind her. She turned and saw a blue-eyed, sandy-haired boy pricking a sheet of paper with a little pointed instrument. Jill was watching too. "That's Braille," she whispered. But Jenny turned away then, not liking to stare even though the boy couldn't know she looked at him.

"July is the high noon of our year," Mr. Dillon was saying, "the month of hot sun and long daylight, of creation and productivity. To help you get the most from it, I have a bit of advice for you. That is, to ask questions. Perhaps you're told at home not to ask so many. Well, here at Greenwood we encourage them. And if we can't always answer, it's good for us to look things up too. But don't just ask us; ask this library—it's yours—and ask your field guides. Ask each other and ask yourselves. 'Why' and 'how' are words I want to hear often. There's a reason for everything in nature, and the reasons are fascinating and important. Look for them. Search for causes. Nature itself will often provide the answer you're after. Maybe you'll discover something no one else ever has. But in any case you'll know *why* and *how* something exists, not simply that it does."

Brian thought, this may turn out to be pretty interesting. He glanced at Toby who was engaged in swinging his foot and gazing out of the window. Brian wondered how much of Mr. Dillon's talk his cousin had listened to.

David Blair was reading over what he had written. His hand moved lightly across the paper, and he looked absorbed.

Jenny wished that Rosalie would come sit with them, but she was in the back of the room with the other counselors. "Do you like your tent?" she asked Jill, feeling a pang of longing.

"Oh, it's all right, I guess," said Jill.

Brian was anxious now to be outside looking for reasons and causes as Mr. Dillon had urged. He thought, I hope this camp isn't going to be mostly talk, and turning restlessly he saw Dan pick up some cards and start for the front of the room.

"Before we go out," Dan began, "Mr. Dillon has asked me to say something about notes, which you'll be taking in the field as well as in the workshop and library. I know you all take notes in school, so I won't go into that kind of note-taking. But I'd like to talk for a minute about field notes on cards. The idea isn't too different from the field notebook, except that the information goes on these three-by-five-inch cards instead of on pages, so it can easily be classified for reference later on."

He must have seen some puzzled expressions then, because he smiled and held up one of the cards. "For example," he explained, "suppose you're taking up turtles. Each species of turtle would have its own card—painted turtle, box turtle, snapping turtle, and so on—but all the cards would go together under the heading 'Turtles,' which in turn goes under 'Amphibians' in your file."

Jenny understood then why he had chosen turtles as his example. And she loved them too, especially the ones that sunned themselves on floating logs in spring.

"Where can you get the cards?" somebody asked.

"We have them for sale here at camp," Dan replied.

"And when you get them, what next?" asked Toby, surprisingly, Brian thought. But Jenny was not surprised; she could imagine him purchasing great quantities. He loved to buy things.

"Then," Dan went on, "you fill in the date, time of day, location, and weather. And the altitude if you know it. That can be important. Then whether the object seems to be facing north or south, and whether it prefers full sun, deep shade, or a combination of the two. Next observe the type of soil around it, and if you have a thermometer, take a reading of the microclimate."

"Of the *what?*" whispered Jill.

"I haven't the vaguest idea," Jenny replied, feeling a little lost.

"Microclimate," Dan was saying, "is a hard word for something easy. It means climate on the smallest scale. But for our purposes let's let it be simply the temperature of the particular object we're studying."

"I didn't come to camp to *study*," Toby told Brian.

"You came to learn, didn't you?"

"I suppose so."

"Well, it's all part of the same thing."

Dan was gathering up his cards. "Of course you'll note the behavior, what your subject seems to be doing, why it's there. And finally, environment. Where is it living, and how does it seem to relate to its surroundings? Is the habitat always the same? Would you find a myrtle warbler in Canada nesting in the same kind of vegetation that it nests in here?"

Brian, interested in this, raised his hand. "Would you?"

44

"This camper," Dan told them all, "is particularly interested in birds. Maybe he'd like to make a survey of nesting
habits as a special project while he's here. That would be a
real addition to our workshop material. I didn't answer your
question, Brian, because I couldn't. You'll have to do some
research and tell *us*. And now let's go out for a walk."

With a great scraping of chairs they stood up. Jenny saw
David reach for his stick and leave with the others. It
seemed wonderful to her that he knew just where everyone
and everything was. At the door she joined him. "Hello,"
she said shyly, "I'm Jenny Vogel. My brother's in your tent."

David Blair turned to her with a smile. "Yes. He told me
about you. He said you were good at bird songs."

Jenny blushed with pleasure. "Oh, Brian's the bird expert.
But I do enjoy their songs."

"So do I. It's the thing about birds I like most. I wish you'd
teach me to recognize some of the ones around Greenwood."

"Why, David, I'd love to help you with them. If you don't
mind that I'm just learning too." She paused. "There's a step
here," she added, going down.

But David had already found it. "Pretty soon I'll know my
way around," he said.

"That was a good talk of Dan's," Brian declared, joining them. Jenny could tell he was already thinking about his special project.

"I didn't understand everything I heard this morning," she admitted, "but maybe I will later on."

"Things'll get clearer when we're out on trips and can see for ourselves," David said. And he started toward the woods with Brian and Toby.

Rosalie, with Jill sticking close to her side, came up to join Jenny. "Isn't David Blair a wonderful boy?" she asked.

"I like him so much," Jenny told her. "He asked me to teach him some bird songs."

"You can learn a lot from David too," Rosalie said thoughtfully.

And the three girls and three boys mingled with the rest of the campers and counselors as they followed Mr. Dillon down the trail.

CHAPTER FIVE

WEATHER AND NESTS

"WHAT'S THE first thing you notice when you wake up in the morning?" Mr. Dillon asked the campers assembled in the workshop.

The sunrise through the trees, thought Jenny.

Brian raised his hand and said, "Birds singing."

"For most of us," Mr. Dillon told them, "it's the weather. It's outside every window and meets you the minute you step outdoors. And a great deal depends on the weather, not just your picnics and baseball games, but most of nature's activities too. Probably no cloud moves overhead without casting a meaningful shadow. I know we take weather pretty much for granted, but now let's see what it really is."

Brian opened the notebook his science teacher had given him, and printed WEATHER at the top of a blank page.

47

"Weather has been called the temperature, pressure, motion, and moisture of the air. It requires atmosphere, that's why we say there's no weather on the moon. Fortunately there is plenty of atmosphere around us. We know that man can survive, if he has to, for about three weeks without food, and about three days without water. How long do you think he could live without air?"

"Three minutes?" suggested David.

"Oh," exclaimed Mr. Dillon, "I hope you'll never have to try to! Hold your breath, all of you, and look at your watches. That's how long you could live without air."

Brian peered out the window at the air he could not really see, and considered it with new respect.

"What would you guess the air weighs?" Mr. Dillon was asking.

Weighs? wondered Jill. "Nothing. How could it?" She lifted her palm as though testing the weight of the air on it.

"This will surprise you, then. At sea level, the air above you presses down at a weight of over fourteen and a half pounds per square inch of surface."

"Square *inch?*" cried Toby. "But we'd be squashed!"

"Flatter than pancakes," agreed the camp director, "if the air inside of us didn't push back at an equal pressure. Consider that, when you take a good deep breath, as I hope you often do."

And Jenny could hear everyone around her breathing deeply.

"It would be natural to think," Mr. Dillon went on, "that the closer you went toward the sun the warmer the air would be. But actually up to a certain point the air gets colder as you go up. Planes have to use defrosters and heaters. The earth stops the sun's rays and re-radiates them, and the density of the atmosphere near the earth's surface retains that warmth."

"I wish I were up in a plane right now, don't you?" Toby whispered.

"Listen to Mr. Dillon," his cousin begged. "It's air, not airplanes, we're supposed to be thinking about."

"Warm air rises, as you probably know, and as it rises it cools, and as it cools the moisture in it condenses to form clouds. Clouds are made of water droplets, ice crystals, or a combination of water-and-ice particles. When the particles are large and heavy enough to fall, we have rain or snow, depending on the temperature of the air. You may not be very fond of rain when it interferes with your outdoor plans, but here at Greenwood we like it because it makes mushrooms and other interesting fungi appear in the woods, and encourages some of the amphibians to come out where we can observe them."

"It waters your garden," added Brian. He knew, because rain had saved him many hours of work in the beds he had planted last summer with flowers and shrubs that attract birds.

"Don't tell me you have a garden!" scoffed Toby.

"What's so strange about that?" David wanted to know. "I have one too."

Mr. Dillon continued, "Songs and poems have been written about clouds, and with good reason, for they are fascinating and ever-changing. We think we see a great white horse in the sky, and, while we look, it turns into a dragon, and then a whale. But clouds are more than just fun to watch; they tell a story. They tell us what tomorrow's weather will be."

If you could read the clouds, thought Jenny, you wouldn't have to listen so often to the forecasts on the radio. She had always enjoyed looking up into the sky. The clouds were better than a kaleidoscope. She especially loved the ones that resemble the beach when the sea has run out over it. And she also loved those pink feathers that curl in the west after the sun has set, and the great scoops of vanilla ice cream that puff along above the horizon on a fine summer day.

"Cirrus, the high clouds; stratus, the low clouds; and cumulus, the rising fair-weather clouds, are the main types for you to remember. The names of the rest are for the most part combinations of these three."

Brian decided that he would keep a day-to-day record of the clouds, and see if he really could predict the weather by them.

Thunderclouds were now being discussed. Jill nudged Jenny because she knew her cousin was afraid of thunderstorms. Perhaps if you didn't see the lightning, they wouldn't seem so bad, Jenny had sometimes thought. "Do you like thunderstorms?" she whispered to David, and, "Yes, I think they're exciting," he whispered back.

"Thunderclouds often reach tremendous heights," Mr. Dillon went on, "and they grow very dark. Look for the anvil-shape across the top if you want to be sure."

But Jenny thought that she did not have to look for anvil-shapes to be sure. She had an instinctive feeling inside of her when these storms were coming.

"Near the earth's surface the air is always moving," Mr. Dillon was telling them, "so that we get quite a mixture of it. Part of the air in this room may have been out over the Pacific not so long ago, and another part over Canada or Mexico. So if you can't go to those places yourself, at least you can think that the air you breathe has been there. And we call this moving air 'wind.' How many of you have ever seen the wind?"

Jenny put her hand up and then down again as she saw that no other hands were going up. "Silly," hissed Jill, "you can't see wind."

"I like to think that you *can*," declared Mr. Dillon. "When I look into the trees on a breezy fall day, or during a March gale, I like to believe I can see the wind there. Its speed is measured like the speed of your car, by miles per hour. And there's a scale you can all use to tell what the wind speed is, from absolute calm, when smoke rises straight up, to hurricane force, more than seventy-five miles an hour, when the wind is strong enough to knock a person down and great damage is done."

"We have hurricanes on Cape Cod," Toby informed the group. "I've been in them, right under the eye."

So have I, thought Brian and Jenny and Jill.

"Then," said Mr. Dillon, "surely you must have thought you could see *those* winds. Observe the trees on open plains, or mountainsides, or forests, and you may be able to tell, from the way the tops are bent, what the prevailing wind direction is. In case of fire, this is a valuable thing to know."

"Dan was talking about a thermometer," he said next. "Well, there's a different kind that you can all have, and it

51

doesn't cost a penny or require any materials but a pair of ears and the ability to count. This is a cricket thermometer, and while it isn't guaranteed to be one hundred percent accurate, it's worthwhile to try. On a warm day count the number of chirps that a cricket gives in fourteen seconds, and then add forty, and you should have more or less the correct temperature of the air, that is, near the cricket at any rate!"

"I've noticed that crickets do chirp faster in warm weather," David remarked to Brian as they left the workshop.

Like the red-eyed vireo's songs, Brian remembered.

That afternoon the campers met in the clearing by the pond, and Dan Alderman divided them into three groups. Brian was left over. You forgot my brother, Jenny thought of saying. Afterwards, though, she was glad she hadn't.

"Birds have always had a special appeal for us because of their beauty of feather and song, and because of the freedom their flight seems to give them. Many people who study the whole field of natural history do so because they were interested first of all in birds; birds seem to lead them on to other things. So this afternoon we're going to concentrate on birds, and take a nesting census of the camp area." Dan unfolded some large sheets of paper and showed them to Brian.

"What's a nesting census?" Jill asked Rosalie. They must be great friends, Jenny thought. They were always together now. She felt a little lonely and left out; she had counted so on Rosalie's being *her* special friend.

"It's a count of the birds' nests we find here," Rosalie answered. "But Dan will explain."

"Group one," Dan was saying, "will cover the deep forest, group two the open clearing and forest edge, and group three the pond and stream."

"That isn't fair," interrupted Toby, who was in the first group. "The forest's by far the biggest."

"But that doesn't mean that more birds nest there. You'll see. I have a map here of the territory for each group. Mark on it the location of every nest you find, what birds built it, whether it is on the ground, in a bush, or in a tree, *what* bush or tree, and whether or not you think it's occupied."

The campers were wide-eyed and wondering even before Dan finished. "How," they asked, almost in unison, "are we supposed to know that?"

"Ah," replied Dan, "we're going to give you expert help."

"Brian," said his cousin.

"Yes. Brian will go with each group to help with identification."

"There should be three Brians," David pointed out.

"That would be fine for Greenwood, but since there aren't he'll start out first with the forest group. Now off you go, and I'm sure I don't have to tell you not to disturb the birds, their eggs, or their young."

Brian felt proud and happy to have been sent with the groups as an expert. "You're really getting to be important around here, aren't you?" Toby asked as they started toward the woods.

"I won't be when they take up things like amphibians," Brian told him modestly.

"Here's a nest!" cried somebody, and the census had begun.

This nest in a young maple tree was much like the one Jenny had seen on the way in to camp. It had paper drinking straws and a bit of tissue woven into it. And the bird, a wood thrush, Brian said, was sitting on it. They could see its dark eye and its beak pointed straight ahead.

A husky robin-like call led them to a brilliant scarlet tanager high in the light oak leaves. Following him, the campers found his nest near the end of a branch, and looking up they thought they could make out three eggs through the thin nest floor.

Where the trail wound among the evergreens, Brian discovered one of the most interesting of all nests, the ovenbird's. The mother was fluttering down the path ahead of him, to attract his attention. And in the oven-shaped shelter sat three fuzzy young ones.

"Come away now," Brian urged the others, but it was hard even for him to leave. I must bring Jenny here, he thought, remembering how she had loved the one that Mr. Crandall had shown them last summer.

When he reached the clearing the group there had already located the nest of tree swallows, in a box put up for them to build in; a robin's nest; and a catbird's, grapevine-lined, in a lilac bush close to the workshop porch. Brian found for them a red-eyed vireo's slung from a crotch in an elm branch, and, not far over their heads, a rose-breasted grosbeak's in the fork of a small white pine at the edge of the woods. As they walked past a low pasture juniper, a towhee sprang up, and there on the ground under the branches was its nest with four white eggs, finely speckled with brown. "You can go searching for nests," Brian told them, "but often you find just as many by chance."

Six inches from the ground in another juniper a hermit thrush was nesting. The nest was deep and compact, and lined with pine needles and moss that was still green. The eggs were robin's-egg blue, but smaller than a robin's and pointed at one end. And how fortunate they were, thought the campers, to come upon the nesting place of the shy hermit, frequenter of the deep woods.

Ever since he had become interested in birds, Brian had hoped to see a hummingbird's nest. Suddenly, right before him, lichen-crusted, saddled on a down-slanting branch, there one was, and so well disguised that it might have been part of the tree. He had read somewhere that the nests were bound to the limbs with spider-webs. And how, he marveled, as thousands had marveled before him, does this tiny creature know how to do that?

The group at the pond and stream had found a kingbird nesting in a bush by the water's edge. The nest had string and feathers in it, and the birds flew about overhead, calling in their high, excited way. Jenny had discovered a phoebe's nest under the bridge. "How did you know it was a phoebe?" they asked her.

"Oh, because we *have* one," she told them proudly, "over a kitchen window at home."

Then Brian showed them a yellow warbler's, beautifully made of silvery fibers and grasses, in an alder by the stream. The birds, called by the country folk "summer yellow-birds," flitted among the branches like golden leaves in an autumn wind.

At the end of the census Dan examined the charts. He asked Brian to mark all the nests on one map and put that one on the workshop wall. "And now," he went on to the others, "where have you concluded most of the nests were?"

"In the clearing," they told him promptly.

"Yes, the clearing which included the forest border, not necessarily the largest area. In fact, in this case, the smallest. So you see, size of territory doesn't really determine the number of nests. I think we can safely say that more birds found the food supply they need, and the kind of nesting site they require, here in this spot than in the other locations you explored. Would you agree with that, Brian?"

And Brian nodded and quietly collected the maps.

Toby, walking back with him, said, "You're quite a hero."

"It was your mother who started me off on birds," Brian reminded him.

"She must be nice," David ventured. "I'd like to know her too."

"She'll probably come up on visiting day," Toby said carelessly.

By the dining hall steps after supper Brian drew his sister aside. "Guess where Toby's baseball bat is now?" he asked.

"Why, I can't imagine," she said, surprised.

"In Mr. Dillon's office. Toby took it out of Dan's foot locker, where it was supposed to be kept, and in swinging it around the tent he came within inches of David's head."

Jenny gasped. That anything like this should happen was unthinkable.

"Of course he didn't mean to," Brian went on. "He said he didn't notice David was there. You know how he doesn't notice things. But Dan told him he had no right to be playing with it when he had already had it taken away once, and that he had barely avoided a serious accident. I think Toby was frightened; anyway he didn't say much. But do you know what David did? He asked Dan not to speak to Mr. Dillon about it because it would be too bad for Toby to get into trouble for something he hadn't meant to do."

CHAPTER SIX

THE FOREST AND THE POND

"In our study of nature," began Mr. Dillon, "let's not forget that *we*, also, are animals. Warm-blooded, reasoning, and, generally considered, intelligent animals. Man is, in fact, the only creature that lives successfully from pole to pole. We have *our* habitats too. Let's go outside and see what kind of habitat we're living in here."

It was always much better, Jenny thought, to be outside. The workshop was nice, and now it had Brian's nest census map on the wall, but there was something about the woods that made you wish to be there rather than indoors.

David said quietly to Brian, "Trees are a sort of specialty of mine. I like them because their bark and leaves and needles are easy to identify, and they stay there and don't fly off while you're trying to study them."

59

"I don't know one tree from another," Brian confessed, though exaggerating his ignorance. "But I want to. It's helpful in birding."

"Oh," said Dan, joining them, "trees are wonderful for themselves. Pretty soon you'll think so too."

"I had my bat taken away again," Toby informed his sister. "This time it's in Mr. Dillon's office."

"Well," Jill said airily, "apparently it wasn't going to do you much good here anyhow." And she skipped ahead to catch up with Rosalie.

The campers sat on the pine needles around Mr. Dillon, some of them leaning back against tree trunks, others bent forward, taking notes. "We are fortunate here at Greenwood," the director told them, "to have our camp located in such a fine forest. Good ones are not hard to find, however. States maintain them for the public, and there are town forests. If you remember what you learn here you will be able to apply it wherever you go. That's one of the satisfying things about nature."

Thrushes called, and, "Zeep, zeep, zeep, zeep, zizi, tzeee," sounded high and thin over their heads.

"Blackburnian warblers like the tall trees. So do some other birds that you're not as apt to find nearer the ground. No, Brian, sit still. I'm sorry, but first we're going to discuss a forest in general; we have weeks ahead to discover its wildlife."

Blackburnian warbler, murmured Brian under his breath, and Jenny sent him a quick look of sympathy because she knew how he would have loved a glimpse of this beautiful flame-throated bird that they had seen only in pictures.

"Our northeastern woods are blessed with a variety of trees. Some of these species also appear in the southern mountains, since northern vegetation was pushed southward by the great glacier. Sometimes you will hear forests called by the names of characteristic trees in them, like oak-hickory, and the Canadian spruce-fir.

"I often think of a forest as being divided into four layers," Mr. Dillon went on, "the first being the groundcover of the forest floor; the second, the shrub layer; the third, the smaller tree tops, or understory; and the fourth and highest, the overstory or canopy."

Jenny remembered an outdoor party where there had been a canopy to cover the guests in case of rain. It was nice to think the woods had a canopy too.

"You are sitting on the forest floor, one of the best places I know to sit. What do you see besides pine needles?"

Rosalie came then and pointed out wild lily of the valley, or Canada mayflower. "Some people call it 'false' lily of the valley, but I think 'wild' sounds better." She showed them

partridgeberry, "Like your tent, Jenny"; bunchberry with a spring flower resembling a tiny dogwood blossom; the dainty starflower; Indian cucumber with its edible root; prince's pine—not a pine at all, but one name for the evergreen pipsissewa; twisted stalk with its rosy bells; and the dark glossy leaves of wintergreen. She bit a leaf and urged them to try some too.

"It tastes like chewing gum," Jill volunteered.

"Well, I suppose that's one way to describe it," Rosalie said. "Groundcovers vary, of course, in different parts of the country, but they are always interesting. You can also see mosses, mushrooms, ferns, and Indian pipes, depending on the season. The forest has a lovely carpet on its floor."

"The shrub layer," Mr. Dillon continued then, "is made up of bushes and low trees. Some that grow here are the viburnums, including hobblebush with its showy white flowers; in damp places the black alder with its bright red berries in the fall; witch hazel that blooms with yellow fringelike flowers in autumn when the other flowers have gone, and throws its seeds two dozen feet away; young moosewood, or striped maple, whose beautiful bark moose like to eat; and shoots of the American chestnut, a magnificent tree that was demolished years ago by a blight. My father had the fun of gathering the nuts when he was a boy. You and I will not have that pleasure."

Jenny was sad to think of all those trees being destroyed, never to grow straight and tall again. "We still have the horse chestnut," Rosalie told her, "in another family, but a very pretty tree."

Jill nodded. On warm fall days she had often collected the shiny brown seeds. Her mother had told her what they were.

"The understory, or the trees that don't quite reach the top, may be said to represent the next generation coming along. Some day many of these may be up in the canopy. You'll notice that quite a few of the lower trees and bushes in the shrub layer have exceedingly large leaves. That is so that they can make the greatest possible use of whatever sunshine filters through the dense shade. A tree that lives happily in the shadow of others is the graceful hemlock. Trees like this are called shade-tolerant.

"Then," Mr. Dillon said, "in the overstory itself are the tallest trees, the ones that have won the battle up into full sunlight. These are the dominant trees of any forest. Here they appear to be white pine, white ash, oaks, maples, and hickory. Some white birches grow quite tall, and are often thought the handsomest of woodland trees. But don't be tempted to peel off the papery bark; it will never grow back again. And now, David, if you'd help us with some identification——," and he placed a bouquet of twigs in David's outstretched hand.

David felt them carefully. "These are evergreens," he said in a moment, "all but this one, the larch, which drops its needles in fall. I can tell it's a larch because the needles grow in soft little tufts along the branch."

"It's a tree that grows as far north as the Arctic Circle," Dan added. "Some people call them tamaracks, an Algonquin Indian name. They turn honey-colored in autumn, before the tufts come off."

"This," went on David, "is a white pine." He held up the twig. "It has five needles in each bunch and five letters in its name, 'white.' This is a red pine, with two long needles in a bunch. And I think this is a spruce because the short, thick needles grow all around the twig, roll easily in your fingers, and are prickly to touch. This must be fir because it smells like a Christmas tree. And this one feels like a hemlock because its short, flat needles grow horizontally on the twig, and do not prickle. And I'd say these last two are cedars, one an arbor vitae with all its needles overlapped like fish scales, and one a red cedar because it also has sharp needles as well as the overlapping ones."

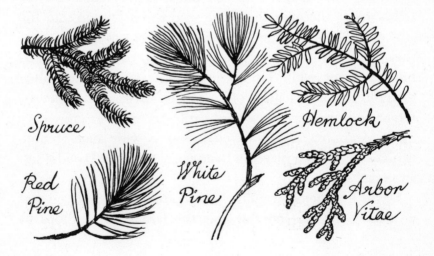

Spruce

Hemlock

Red Pine

White Pine

Arbor Vitae

Jenny was very proud of David. "Would you say these conifers, trees with cones, are easy to identify?" Mr. Dillon was asking him.

"Yes. That wasn't hard."

"Then I hope," said Mr. Dillon, "that we'll have no one here at Greenwood who calls every evergreen he sees a pine. No, don't sit down, David. I have some leaves for you."

"Oh, gosh," protested David, embarrassed, but he knew them right away, and told the other campers first how to identify the sugar maple leaf, "The notches between the lobes are u-shaped, think of the *u* in sugar," and the red maple, "The notches are v-shaped, think of the *v* in vermilion, a shade of red.

"And these are oak leaves," he went on, "good to know because the oaks are almost everywhere. This must be the white oak because the lobe feels deep and round, five letters in both 'white' and 'round,' and this the red with pointed lobes. The lobe is the part of the leaf that curves out, like an ear lobe."

"We have the biggest oak in the whole world growing near our farm in Maryland," Toby announced.

"Your part of the country has many fine trees," Mr. Dillon told him, "including the towering tulip poplar. Well, David, what else is useful in identifying trees?"

"I think the bark, that's so smooth on the beech, and shaggy on the shagbark hickory; and the sound of the leaves too. The beech's crackle, and the trembling aspen's are in motion at the slightest breeze. And sometimes you can tell by tasting twigs, like the mitten-leaf—I mean sassafras—tree, and the black birch, and black cherry."

65

A tiny frog nearly hopped into Jenny's lap. It was a lovely chocolate-brown, and seemed to have a little black mask across its eyes. "A young wood frog," said Dan. And just the place for it to be, thought Jenny, remembering then another masked favorite, the northern yellow-throat.

"I don't have to tell you," Mr. Dillon concluded, "that one morning is hardly long enough to spend talking about a forest. Even a lifetime is too short for all that can be learned. But notice trees in every season, and learn their names and characteristics, and they will become old friends that will usually be right there when you come back the next time."

"He didn't believe me about that oak," Toby said to Brian. "Well, the 'whole world's' pretty big," his cousin told him.

"I wish I could show it to him. Then he'd have to believe it."

And Brian thought, how marvelous if Mr. Dillon, and Dan and David too, could come down to Cousin Laura's. What a wonderful place that would be for a Greenwood reunion!

"If I could have anything I wanted in my backyard," Rosalie said, "I'd have a pond."

Ours at home is *almost* in our backyard, thought Jenny, pleased.

"It's an entire little world of its own," Rosalie went on, "a perfect setting to study what life is and means."

"Life on this earth began in water," said Dan, "and many of the simpler forms of plants and animals can still be found there."

They were standing by the edge of the Greenwood pond. At their approach the male towhee, formal and neat, had sprung up from the juniper above its nest. A Canada warbler, with slate-blue back, yellow breast, and fine black "necklace," was calling jubilantly from the alders. Swallows clicked in the air over the water, and, "Pretty bird, pretty bird," sang a brown thrasher from the top of a spruce. Pretty *world*, said Jenny to herself.

"We thought of a forest as having four layers," Rosalie began. "Let's think of a pond as having three, the part beneath the surface, the surface itself, and what is around and above the surface."

"Does everything in nature have to come in layers?" asked Jill. They made her think of a cake, and she was hungry.

Frogs, that had plunged into the water at the arrival of the campers, now began to reappear on the pads of the fragrant white water lilies and yellow spatterdock. "Jug o' rum," croaked the bullfrogs, puffing out their lemon-colored throats. And the green frogs sounded just like banjos. An electric-blue damsel fly sped past, and handsome red admiral butterflies came daintily to the margins to drink.

"Did you know that a pond turns over in spring?" Dan was asking.

"Turns over?" echoed Brian.

"When the water at the surface freezes, it stays on top. Like a blanket it keeps an even warmth below the surface where much life activity still goes on. As it thaws, the cold, melted ice sinks to the bottom, and the warmer water that was underneath comes to the top. That's why we say it turns over."

"And the pond gives off water as vapor," Rosalie added. "This rises, and condenses in the coolness of the air to form clouds and perhaps rain, which falls back into the pond, completing the circle."

"Look," exclaimed Toby, "here's an animal track! What made that?"

"I'd guess a raccoon," Dan said. "If you wished to preserve it, you could let wax from a lighted candle fall into the impression of the footprint. When the wax was dry it would lift out. Then you could make a plaster cast from it at home if you wanted to."

A female dragonfly was laying eggs in the water; like a seamstress, Jenny thought, watching as it dipped steadily along, poking its tail into the surface and then raising it, depositing egg after egg.

Dan had waded out into the pond, taking a wooden box with a screen in it that he called a bottom-scraper. Immediately everyone else wanted to wade too. But, "No," explained Rosalie, "you'd stir up too much mud, and none of us would be able to see anything. Dan will come back and show us what he finds. Look, did you know that fish build nests?"

"They do not," contradicted Toby.

"Shhh. See for yourself." And sure enough, where the water was shallow, sunfish, having cleared round or oval places among the grasses on the bottom, hovered, fanning with their turquoise-edged tails and fins, protecting and cleaning their nests.

"Let's see what's growing in and around the pond," Rosalie suggested, and she showed them the bright-green floating duckweed, one of the smallest of all flowering plants; the arrowhead, with its arrow-shaped leaves and white flowers, whose tubers the Indians used as food; stately blue pickerelweed; wild flag, like a delicate garden iris; sedges with their triangular stems, and rushes with their round ones. "The clearer the water, the more plants are able to grow there," she added.

Solomon's seal bent its leaves down a bank. "It's called that because the scars of earlier stems on the rootstock are said to resemble the ancient seals used in Biblical days. If you count the scars, or seals, you can figure out the age of the plant."

Dan was coming back with his sieve. It was really more like a window screen with sides, so that the tiny animals could run around and not get out. "I have a newt," he called, and they all crowded to see this salamander with its short

69

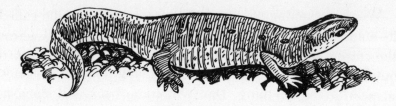

legs and long tail and red and black spots on a greenish-brown back. "And here're lots of tadpoles, and these are water striders——"

"There's another too," and Jenny pointed toward the pond. On the glistening sand beneath six dots appeared, shadows of the dimples that the feet of the insect made on the surface.

"And here's a water boatman rowing, and this is a back swimmer," Dan was saying. "Back swimmers, lying on their backs, paddle about and hang from the surface with their heads down, looking for food. Both of these species have strong hind legs which they use like oars. They're able to stay for long periods beneath the water. And sometimes in spring the male boatman will make a chirping sound by rubbing his front legs together. These whirligig beetles, spinning round and round, usually travel in groups. Some people say they smell of vanilla."

"They're certainly well named," Jenny told David. "Even on that screen they're whirling about." And she described to him the pinkish, semi-transparent fairy shrimp, the pond snails, the squirming tadpoles, and the cylindric and rectangular caddis fly cases, used by the fly's larvae for a home made of sand and bits of twigs, pebbles, and shells—whatever could be found in the water.

70

Where a running stream—a miniature river, Rosalie called it—emptied into the pond, caddis flies had woven nets across the current to catch food. Upstream a painted turtle slipped quietly off the bank into the brook. The phoebe darted, snapped at something in the air, and sat on a low branch, swinging its tail. Dan was showing them a fierce-looking wriggly creature in the palm of his hand. "That's a hellgrammite, the larva, or immature form, of the Dobson fly. You find them under rocks in fast-moving water." The campers thought "hellgrammite" a very funny name, and while they were laughing about it, Brian suddenly cried, "A snake!" and they all rushed to the edge of the stream, and some of them *into* the stream.

"Catch it!" the boys called, which was just what Brian, with a stick, was trying to do. But the snake, sleek and swift as an arrow, shot away.

"What did it look like?" asked David with great interest, as excited as the others.

"Oh," murmured Jenny, "I'm afraid I didn't see it." She couldn't tell him that she didn't like snakes, and therefore hadn't even *tried* to see it.

And David looked so disappointed then that Jenny felt ashamed of herself for not having watched when she could have.

Wide awake that night, Jenny stood outside her tent and gazed up at the stars that looked so big and low they seemed to be caught in the very tree tops. She could hear the frogs down at the pond, and far in the distance a whip-poor-will. She thought of her parents, and Cousin Laura, and wondered what they were doing now.

A flashlight shone through the woods; the way it appeared and then disappeared behind the trunks made it resemble a firefly, on and off, on and off. But it was Rosalie, who came asking, "Ought you to be outside?"

"I was just looking at the stars."

"We'll have a special night for star study. You should be in your tent now and going to sleep."

"I wish *you* were in my tent," Jenny said wistfully.

"Oh, but you have such nice people in yours. Now, do go to bed, won't you?" and with a wave of her hand she was gone.

Not as nice as you, Jenny would like to have said, standing there a little lonely in the dark. Then she looked up again. Over her head was the bright blue-white star Vega, in the constellation of the Lyre. Seeing it, and recognizing it, a companion of many warm evenings, she felt reassured and no longer wistful or alone.

CHAPTER SEVEN

INSECTS, AMPHIBIANS
AND REPTILES

"BRING YOUR insect nets when we meet at the workshop," Mr. Dillon announced at breakfast. "Today we're going on a butterfly hunt."

"Oh, no!" protested Toby.

"There'll be plenty of other insects too," Dan told him encouragingly. "After all, there are supposed to be over twelve thousand to every human being. And summertime is insect time."

Jenny thought that a butterfly hunt sounded like lots of fun, but her brother wasn't so sure.

"Butterflies may be all right for girls," Toby grumbled to him on their way back to the tent, "but you won't catch *me* running around with a net."

And Brian, watching two boys hurry past swinging at everything they saw, was inclined to agree.

"What are you going to do instead?" he wanted to know, and Toby declared that he intended to return to the pond to look for the water snake. "You'd better come too," he said, "unless, of course, you're just dying to chase butterflies."

"They'll be very angry when they find out," Brian objected, doubtful and hesitant.

"They may not even miss us. And anyway if we catch that snake for the workshop aquarium they'll be too grateful to punish us."

But Brian thought he wouldn't mind being punished as much as he'd mind displeasing Mr. Dillon and Dan.

"Come on," urged Toby. "This isn't school where you have to go to every class. This is camp that you're only supposed to come to at all because you want to."

Mr. Dillon took the rest of the campers to an open field at the other side of the forest. The air was alive with insects. Bees, proverbially busy, zoomed by. 'On days that are sunny they're making their honey,' thought Jenny. Wasps swung overhead. Froghoppers had made bubbly foam on stems and grasses; the children enjoyed looking for the tiny green bugs in the froth. Dainty lacewings, bluebottle flies, yellow jackets, and ladybird beetles, also called ladybugs, moved freely here and there. Grasshoppers jumped in arcs of light. Ants

scurried about an ant hill. Somebody found a walking stick, one of the finest examples of nature's protective shaping and coloration, and somebody else found a praying mantis. "Though it isn't really praying," Dan said, "but waiting to pounce on an unfortunate victim."

"Wherever man has gone, insects have preceded him," Mr. Dillon told them. "There are more kinds of insects than all other animal species put together. Did you know, by the way, that spiders are not insects?"

This came as a surprise to most of them. Not insects? wondered Jenny, and even David thought it was strange. "Insects always have six legs," Dan explained. "Spiders have eight. This puts them in another class entirely."

"Ants and bees," said Mr. Dillon, "were organizing communities long before we knew how to. Ants, with their intricate colonies which include workers, beggars, thieves, road-makers, soldiers, nurses, and royal families, are in their social and domestic ways the most like people. Bees, flies, and butterflies are the predominant pollinators. Wildflowers and other plants depend on them for their existence, and so does the soil where the plants grow and stop erosion."

"Erosion," Dan added, "is the wearing away of good soil by wind, and by water running through it."

Of all the insects that morning, the butterflies, floating on the summer air, were what the campers enjoyed most. Along the forest edge danced the little wood satyrs, with blue-eyed graylings and mourning cloaks nearby. Meadow fritillaries, painted ladies, and red-spotted purples brightened the field. "Don't you adore the names?" said Rosalie. Tiger swallowtails gathered at a puddle. "They hold mud puddle parties," Dan pointed out, "where they suck the mud for nourishment. They also seem to like tobacco smoke, and hover around the pipes of fishermen on the banks of rivers and streams."

White cabbage butterflies, the despair of farmers; yellow sulphurs, that also flock to mud puddles; coppers; and spring azures flitted over wide beds of bluets that patterned the meadow like patches of snow in March. "The spring azure, such a welcome sight at the end of winter, has several broods," Rosalie told them. "Each hatch produces a lighter-colored specimen until by midsummer some may be nearly white. This butterfly is said to have the odor of crushed violets!"

Then she and Dan showed them how to catch butterflies in nets, and how, when they had looked at them, to let them go again. "Once you have spreading boards and mounts and are ready to start a collection, you may keep a sample of each kind you catch. But here at Greenwood we don't believe in killing or picking anything except for special study purposes."

"Butterflies only live for a day," said Jill, "so what difference does it make?"

"Most butterflies *are* relatively short-lived," Dan answered. "But the idea that they all live for just one day is nothing but a myth."

"Look at that summerhouse!" Jenny exclaimed. And what a funny place for one, she thought, out here in this field.

"Oh, that's a butterfly house," Mr. Dillon told her. "It does look like a summerhouse, square and made of screens, but it's a place for studying butterflies, their life histories, and food plants. The idea for it came from the tropical jungles of British Guiana and Trinidad."

Inside the butterfly house a clump of milkweed was growing. "That's for the monarch, which, as a striped caterpillar, eats the leaf and hangs there its beautiful chrysalis, its 'little green house with golden nails.' From this 'little house' it emerges as the handsome black and orange butterfly, with the powerful sailing flight, that migrates from Ontario to the Gulf of Mexico. Scientists have discovered this by banding them."

"How could you ever band a butterfly?" Jenny wanted to know, thinking of the minute, hair-like legs.

"By fastening a small piece of specially-made gummed paper over the right forewing, near the body. This paper has a number on it. Records are kept of when and where the butterfly was banded, and when it is caught again it's possible to tell both how far and how fast it has come."

"Does it hurt it to be banded?" Jenny had to ask.

"No, it seems to hurt neither the butterfly nor its flying ability."

Also inside the screen house were violet plants for great spangled fritillaries, thistles for painted ladies, nettles for red admirals and certain tortoise shells, lupines, clovers, wisteria, willow shoots, and many grasses. In addition there were mounted specimens showing the life cycles from egg to adult.

"Butterflies are the hardest of all for me," David confessed to Jenny. "But I think their life cycles are awfully interesting."

And Jenny, who had just decided the life cycles were too difficult for her to understand, resolved to study them also.

"I wonder," she said suddenly, "where Brian is."

"He didn't come on the insect trip, did he?" David observed.

Her brother, Jenny thought with pride, was probably working on some special bird project for the camp.

"Hurricanes," Mr. Dillon was saying, "bring before them foreign southern butterflies on high air currents. You could almost foretell a hurricane by these arrivals alone."

"What's the difference," David asked, "between a butterfly and a moth?"

"One difference is that butterflies seek sunlight and bright flowers, while most moths prefer the shade and darkness, flying mainly at night. Butterflies are apt to rest with their wings folded upright over them; moths droop their wings out flat when at rest. Probably the best way to tell them apart is by the antennae. A butterfly's are thin and end in a knob, while a moth's have no knob and are often feathery. Some evening we'll mix up a batch of molasses, sugar, fruit, and beer, and see what the moths think of that."

Brian and Toby, all morning at the pond, caught not so much as a glimpse of the water snake. At noon, they walked slowly back to their tent, Brian, filled with misgivings, wondering what was going to happen to them.

That afternoon Dan told the campers about his particular favorites. "Reptiles and amphibians," he began, "once roamed the earth as kings. The first animals with backbones to leave the water for the land were the amphibians. The great dinosaurs were reptiles, and for a long time they ruled the world. Today these classes contain animals the size of frogs and turtles, still cold-blooded, their temperatures always changing with the temperatures around them. You've seen snakes and turtles heating their bodies on warm surfaces. Warm-blooded animals, on the other hand, no matter how cool the air, maintain an even body temperature. Ours, as you probably know, is normally 98.6°.

"The word 'amphibian' comes from two Greek words, 'amphi' meaning 'of both kinds,' and 'bios' standing for 'life.' Amphibians, which consist of frogs, toads, and salamanders, usually spend the early part of their lives in water, breathing through gills. Then they absorb these and move to the land, often returning to the water to lay their eggs in jelly-like masses. Some frogs, like the bull and the green, may live in the water all their lives.

"Reptiles, which include crocodiles, alligators, turtles, lizards, and snakes, lay their eggs on land. The young emerge looking like small adults, and ready, as a rule, to live like them. Unlike most amphibians, their skin is dry and scaly. Snakes are not slimy, whatever you may have heard."

"I'd never get close enough to one to find out," Jill said loftily to Jenny, and Jenny couldn't help agreeing with her.

Dan took them then on a short walk through the woods, where, turning over rocks and logs, he found for them their first spotted salamander, shiny and black, with bright yellow

dots. Brian and the other boys in his tent were particularly excited with it.

They discovered a coral-colored eft, the red land stage of the newt that they had seen at the pond. "People used to believe the red eft was closely associated with elves and fairies," Dan said, and Jenny, finding it almost unreal in its jewel-like beauty, could understand why.

They uncovered other salamanders, the dusky and the red-backed, and some of the boys began turning over every log in sight. "Always put them back the way they were," Dan cautioned, "whether here at camp or at home. In that way they may still be used by these amphibians." He found an American toad and showed them how it differed from the frogs, with its rough skin, its eggs in strings instead of masses, and its life on land. "Don't believe," he added, "that you'll get warts if you touch one. This is only a fable. Those warty looking places are glands that secrete an irritating substance to protect the toad from its enemies."

"Toad of Toad Hall," said Jenny, remembering a favorite book. And, "Oh," David declared at once, "I've read that one over and over."

"Tree toads and spring peepers," Dan went on, "have sticky pads on their toes that enable them to climb trees in summer after they leave the ponds and marshes where we hear them in the spring."

They saw a wood turtle and a box turtle, but no snakes. "Those will come later," Dan promised, "at the snake farm."

Snake farm! thought Jenny in alarm, but Brian looked pleased.

Brian, however, was not to go. Neither was Toby. This was their punishment for having missed the butterfly hunt. "But," pleaded Brian, "the snake farm was what I most wanted to see."

"I'll stay and you can go in my place," his sister offered.

"Brian and Toby will straighten up the workshop while the rest of us are gone," Mr. Dillon told them. "If they have any time left over they can do some reading in the library. They know why they have to be punished, and there's no need to discuss it. But I'm very much disappointed." And he looked regretfully at Brian.

At the farm there were small snakes in glass jars with sieve tops, and large snakes in screened cages on the ground. All were harmless, and the children were allowed to handle

81

them gently if they wanted to. Only Jenny hadn't the courage, though she had learned through David's enjoyment of them to look once in a while.

"Oh, Jenny, they do feel nice," said David. He was holding a dark one called an indigo that must have been six feet long, and it kept moving constantly through his fingers as though playing a game with him. "Those make good pets," Dan observed, and Jenny could imagine her mother's face if Brian ever brought one home.

The snake's forked tongue flicked out like lightning. Sometimes it brushed David's cheek, and he said it tickled. "Since they have no ears, they use their tongues to catch vibrations," Dan told them, "and also to help in smelling. The milk snake is a good mouser," he added, and, thought Jenny, her mother might almost like that one. David was holding a milk snake now, and she had to admit that it was rather handsome with its markings of chestnut, black, and gray. She described the colors to David. But, oh, she sighed to herself sadly, Brian should be here.

"Snakes protect themselves from enemies in many ways," Dan was saying, "by their blending coloration, by biting, by playing dead, by puffing up and looking ferocious, by their venom if they are poisonous, and by squeezing if they are constrictors. Lizards can make a getaway by dropping their tails, and later growing new ones. Turtles have their shells and their color for protection; frogs have legs developed for leaping; toads have their distasteful fluid; and the newt has an acid skin. So reptiles and amphibians are given their special aids to survival as ancient and important inhabitants of the natural world."

In the tent called Spotted Salamander, David put a small writhing object on Brian's bunk. It was a little green snake. Brian's eyes brightened. "Where did this come from?" he asked.

"From the snake farm," David told him. "They let me handle them. I slipped this one into my pocket when I hoped everybody was paying attention to something else. It seemed too bad to have you miss them all when you like them so much."

Brian had a funny feeling as he sat there playing with his new pet. He couldn't quite understand why David should have done this for him; he certainly hadn't deserved it. And although he knew that he would not be able to keep the snake, that it would have to be returned to the farm, for a little while at least he would have the fun of stroking its smoothness, and watching its swift movements and the light on its shining scales. He thought to himself as he played that he had never had so good a friend as David Blair.

And when he told Jenny what David had done for him, she knew that after this she would not be able to be afraid of snakes ever again.

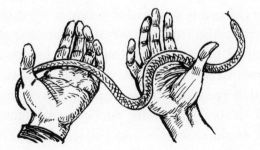

CHAPTER EIGHT

A PLANT PARADE, A RUNAWAY,
AND A NEW BIRD

"DID YOU ever see a plant parade?" Rosalie asked the campers.

"How could plants march?" demanded Toby. "They can't even move."

"And yet their seeds," she told him, "travel great distances. Some of us say that people are the greatest travelers, others believe birds are. But some plant families have been all around the world. They travel on ships and on trains, in the hair and wool of animals, inside of birds, and on the wind. Some seeds, the maple's for instance, are winged to help them through the air. And thistles and dandelions have silky parachutes attached to their seeds that send them sailing away.

"Our plant parade, however, will not actually move, like a seed. It will progress, by examples that we find here at Greenwood, from the earth's earliest and most primitive plant forms to our complex and beautiful wildflowers."

As Rosalie said "beautiful wildflowers," Toby turned and sent Brian an eloquent look of boredom. But Brian thought that this topic might turn out to be quite interesting.

"Leading the plant parade are the algae, the fungi, and the lichens, because these grew first of all on the earth. Think, if you like, of seaweed when I say algae, because that's what the seaweeds are. The scum on ponds is made of algae too. Fungi lack the green coloring of other plants. Mushrooms are among the easiest fungi to see, and have such interesting descriptive names as brownie-cap, fairy-ring, and jack-o-lantern. Lichens are a combination of algae and fungi living together. They are the only plants we know that are able to grow on bare rocks. In a wide variety of places they can almost always be found, with their formations of cunning pyxie cups and British soldiers with scarlet hats."

And Jenny made a mental note to be sure to ask Rosalie to show her a British soldier and a pyxie cup.

"You all must have found mossy places under the trees where the ground was like a velvet carpet. These carpets are made by many separate plants growing side by side. Examine a patch with a magnifying glass or hand lens; it will look like a miniature forest. Have you ever heard of a liverwort?" she asked next.

Jill and some of the other girls wrinkled their noses.

"'Wort' is an old Anglo-Saxon word meaning 'herb'," Rosalie explained. "And liverworts have a very important place in our plant parade. For they are believed to be the first green plant able to live on the land. And we still have them today. They grow on wet, shaded rock walls, and there are some here in Greenwood Forest. When we go out I'll show them to you."

David was taking notes quickly and neatly. Brian had already filled his notebook, and had used up half a pack of field cards.

"Our earliest trees," Rosalie was saying, "were the giant club mosses, horsetails, and ferns that flourished in the great coal forests long before any flowers appeared on earth. Today our club mosses, horsetails, and most of our ferns are very small by comparison. Only in the damp tropics can we still see tree ferns. Club mosses include the ground cedar and running pine. They resemble tiny evergreens and grow on the forest floor. Horsetails, sometimes called scouring rushes, tend to be bushy or feathery and are found mostly in sandy or waste places."

"Do they look like a horse's tail?" Brian wanted to know. He had ridden both show and work horses at Cousin Laura's farm.

Rosalie smiled. "I guess you could say the field horsetail does. With many of these natural history names you have to use some imagination, just as the men who chose them must have done.

"If I ever have time to specialize in one type of plant, I think I'll select the ferns. They were the giants of the world's first forest. And there are only a hundred or so different kinds——"

Only a hundred! thought Jenny.

"——compared with the thousands of flowering plants. And they are so decorative. Today on our field trip I'll introduce you to just a few of the more usual ones. You can go on from there by yourselves.

"And now we are nearing the end of our plant parade. After the ferns come the seed plants, which we divide into the conifers, that you have already studied, and the flowering plants. The flowering plants were the last to appear, and because they had seeds they multiplied rapidly. Now they are almost everywhere."

Jenny tried without success to think what it would be like without a single flower to see or smell. She was glad she didn't have to live in such a world.

"Trees," Rosalie concluded, "such as oaks, elms, maples, and willows, have charming blossoms, and so have many grasses, but as a rule when we think of flowers, we think either of the garden or the wild variety. Some of these, such as the aster, black-eyed susan, and sunflower, are really made up of whole bunches of tiny separate flowers. We call this group the composites. They are the most advanced flower forms, and, though it's hard to believe that a daisy could surpass an oak, in our plant parade the composites march at the very head, or bring up the rear, depending upon how you look at it."

The campers scattered then in groups into the woods and fields to search for samples of all the plant types. Jenny's group found the pyxie cups and British soldiers right on the

St. John's-wort
Wild Geranium
Blue Vervain

ground. I must have walked on them many times without noticing them, she thought, but I'm sure I never shall again.

Her brother discovered liverworts growing in the cool ravine where the brook tumbled down the steep rocks. The translucent little plants looked like bits of sodden lettuce. And Brian felt a stirring of awe as he held in his hand a descendant of the first green growing thing ever to dare attempt to bridge the gap between the sea and the land.

Rosalie showed the fern group the bracken that they could pick and wear turned upside down as a shading coolie hat; the smooth evergreen Christmas fern; the New York fern, tapered at both ends; the distinctive sensitive fern with its broad fronds; the pale, soft hay-scented fern, so fragrant in the sun; the dainty polypody growing on boulder ledges; and the stately cinnamon fern whose fronds bear the spice-colored down used for the lining of hummingbirds' nests.

The wildflower group found few blossoms in the woods. Except for the glowing wood lily, the shinleaf with its waxy white bells, and the welcome fireweed that moves in to cover the burnt forest bareness, flowers were scarce indeed. "Most woodland species bloom early," Rosalie explained, "while the sun can still reach them, before the leaves come too far out on the trees overhead. By July you'll find many more wildflowers in the open fields and along roadsides."

Queen
Anne's
lace

Vetch

Bittersweet
Nightshade

And it was true. There in full sunlight bloomed the meadowsweet, like the palest pink candles; its relative, the rosier
steeplebush; the perfumed dogbane; yellow St.-John's-wort;
wild geranium, also called crane's-bill because the seed pod
resembles the bill of a crane; vervain; the citron-colored mus-
tards; four-leafed loosestrife; Queen Anne's lace, cultivated
in Europe for over a thousand years; graceful blue vetch;
and the gaudy hawkweeds, the tawny one known as devil's
paintbrush.

By a stone wall climbed purple nightshade, bearing red
berries at the same time that it blossomed. Beside it stood the
pale evening primrose whose lemon-smelling flowers are
often visited by moths which avoid the sun as do the flowers
themselves, opening mostly at dusk or on cloudy days. "The
primrose moth," Rosalie told them, "is said to sleep with its
head buried in the blossom." And she showed them the lovely
jewelweed, called touch-me-not because in the fall its seeds
scatter so easily on contact. "It has a reason for its name of
jewelweed too," she said. "Hold a leaf underwater; it will
turn to silver. Tiny hairs, trapping the air, perform this magic
for a plant already fascinating with its yellow-orange spurred
blossoms like tiny elfin caps."

"Aren't wildflowers nothing but weeds after all?" Jill ques-
tioned.

89

"A weed," began Rosalie, "is supposed to be an undesirable or useless plant. Or a plant out of place. But it really depends on who's speaking of it. This shepherd's-purse, for instance," and she broke a slight and insignificant-looking stem, "is considered a nuisance by farmers and gardeners. But look at the little heart-shaped fruits on slender stalks.

They are formed like the money pouches English shepherds used to hang from their belts. And see, when you open them, all the seeds like tiny coins. There's a British poem about this plant that tells of the wealth in seeds that will grow flowers, and adds,

> 'But you cannot grow a pound
> From a farthing in the ground.'"

It was while they were setting up their plant parade on a long table in the workshop that Jill suddenly said, "Where's Toby?"

"He was in my group," David told her, "the fern group." But now he was nowhere to be found

"Where did you boys go the day of the butterfly hunt?" Dan asked Brian, and, still remorseful at the thought of it, Brian answered, subdued, "Just to the pond, no farther than that. He's probably in the tent," he added, but Dan had already looked for him there.

Mr. Dillon, all seriousness, came into the workshop then,

and called Dan aside. "His baseball bat's gone," he said. "It's no longer in my office."

Jill, who had been listening to them, grasped at once what this meant. "He's run away!" she announced admiringly. She seemed not at all worried about her brother's safety. "He might have asked me to go along with him though," she added, a bit annoyed.

The news that Toby Ashton had run away from Greenwood filled the campers with more excitement than alarm. For in spite of the grave faces of the counselors, Toby's friends couldn't believe that any misfortune could befall him. And, as it turned out, they were right. They were told an hour later that he had been found at a soda fountain in the nearby town. "Eating a hot dog, I'll bet," said Brian. Dan, laughing in relief, admitted this was true.

Mr. Dillon, however, did not think it was funny. "The campers, while they are here, are our responsibility," he said. "They are not supposed to leave Greenwood Forest without a counselor, let alone go all the way to town. This shouldn't have been allowed to happen, and I'm very much disturbed."

Dan looked disturbed then too, and he walked out with Mr. Dillon.

"Boy, am I glad I wasn't in on *that* one," Brian confessed.

"Oh, but you *wouldn't* have," breathed his sister, and David said at once, "Of course he wouldn't."

Jill wondered what they would do to her brother, but Toby said he didn't care what happened to him. Plants were boring, he asserted, and he believed he'd had enough of camp.

"Are you sure you mean that?" asked Mr. Dillon. He had taken Toby into his office. And when Toby nodded firmly he picked up the telephone on his desk. "Shall I call your father and ask him to come to see you? Would you like that?"

"My father's dead," Toby told him.

"I'm very sorry, Toby. Your mother, then?"

And when Toby nodded again, Mr. Dillon put through the call to Truro.

"Brian," gasped his sister the next day, "there's Cousin Laura!" She couldn't have been more surprised.

"Yes," Brian told her soberly, "she's come to take Toby home." And he went back to the tent to see if he could help his cousin pack.

"We'll miss you very much," David was saying. "It won't seem the same without you."

"I guess I'm just not the camp type," Toby admitted. "I'm sorry if I caused any trouble, but I didn't want to come in the first place."

Neither did I, Brian remembered, amazed.

At the sight of her mother, Jill burst into tears. "Oh, take me too!" she begged, clinging to her, no longer grown-up.

"Why, Jill," pleaded Rosalie, "you can't go. What would

we ever do without you? I'd miss you dreadfully. I don't know how I'd manage if you went now."

Jenny could hardly believe her ears. And later, after her cousin had been persuaded to stay, she had to protest to Rosalie, "It isn't fair. She's not even particularly interested in nature." But she was ashamed of herself, because she knew why she was saying it. She had wanted Rosalie for *her* friend, and instead she seemed to be Jill's.

"Jenny, Jenny," Rosalie told her gently, "I know things don't always seem fair. We pay a lot of attention to one person and seem to disregard another who may be much more deserving. I don't understand it all myself, but it seems that there are some people you just have to make a greater effort with. It doesn't mean that we like them better, or that they *are* better; it's usually just the opposite. But they seem to need more help. Others, like you, just go their own way and make things easy and pleasant for everybody. And we don't worry much about you, or do much for you, I guess you think. But when the season's over and we're all back home again, you're the ones we remember with the most appreciation."

Jenny, musing about what Rosalie had said, took a short walk alone. She still felt a little ashamed, but she felt happy too, for she knew that something warm and meaningful had been revealed to her. Hardly noticing where she went, she wandered along the rocky stream, where the water ran swiftly past moss-covered logs. She thought of the mosses that had come so early in the parade of plants over the earth. They had discovered one this morning called hair-cap. Daydreaming of Rosalie and of the mosses they had talked about, she

93

found herself looking all of a sudden at a little bird that tilted and teetered by the edge of the brook. A spotted sandpiper, she said with pleasure, remembering the ones that Cousin Laura had taught her last summer. But she had only to look once more to see that, although the bird bobbed up and down, it could not be the spotted sandpiper because, for one thing, it wasn't spotted but striped, and, for another, it was smaller and quite a different shape. Brian will know, she thought at once, and she hurried off to find him.

When they returned the bird was still there, although Brian, in that definite way of his, had been certain it would be gone. It was moving about in a leisurely manner, hunting for food under the leaves that drifted across the rocks. It would pick up a leaf in its bill, and then thrust it aside, like a woman in a hat shop, rejecting hat after hat, thought Jenny. "It's a water thrush," her brother announced, "the one with the white eye-stripe, see it? But I can't remember which that is. Don't say anything to anybody yet, till I've had a chance to look it up." And he darted off exuberantly to find it in his bird book.

CHAPTER NINE

THE QUAKING BOG AND
A MOTH HUNT

FOR SEVERAL days they had talked of nothing but the bog. A field trip was planned. Rosalie and Dan were to be leaders; even Mr. Dillon was going along. "But what's so special about a bog?" Jill wanted to know.

Jenny had been privately thinking the same thing. It seemed to her that bogs were something her mother had always cautioned her to keep out of. Yet here they were, starting off with all the excitement of a real expedition, and equipped with boots, notebooks, and insect repellent. They had even been told to wear a hat.

"This is my favorite trip," said David, who had been coming to Greenwood for two years now. "I always look forward to it. The trees quake when you jump."

This remark made absolutely no sense to Jenny, and she was about to ask him to explain, when he held up his hand. "Listen," he said.

They had come to the place by the stream where Jenny and Brian had seen the bird that teetered. "I thought I heard——," David began, but then he paused and looked baffled.

"What?" asked Jenny and her brother together, intent.

"Well, I didn't know they had them up here, but it *sounded* like a Louisiana water thrush."

Brian and Jenny exchanged glances. "It *was* a Louisiana water thrush," Brian told him. "I saw it the other day and looked it up. But I didn't hear a bird just now."

"Neither did I," admitted Jenny. She thought of telling David that she had been the one to find it; then she decided not to. Birds meant so much to Brian.

"I sometimes do hear things other people don't," David said, and then he grinned and added, "I have to do some of my seeing with my ears."

The walk down to the end of the forest was pleasant on a hot summer day. The pine branches smelled sweet in the sun, ferns looked cool and green, and the stream murmured through half-submerged leaves. Squirrels chattered and scolded as the group passed, and whitethroats in the distance sang of their "sweet Canada." Baby wood thrushes were begging for food. And high over their heads a black-throated green warbler buzzed dreamily.

They came at last to a hillside field full of yarrow and meadowsweet, with butterflies drifting here and there. A cuckoo called from the depth of a gnarled apple tree. While the campers sat in the shade, Mr. Dillon explained about bogs. "If you know something about them beforehand," he said, "it will make it more interesting for you when you go in. Bogs are a present to us from the great glacier. In its movement south, as it swept vegetation away before it, it carved out deep potholes. On their rocky surfaces lichens found a foothold, and on the lichen foundation mosses and ferns gradually took root, and at last other plants. Ice from the glacier, and then rain, slowly filled up these holes. With little or no drainage the water remained very cold. We say that bogs have a cold microclimate.

"Plants from around the edge of the bog began to fill in toward the center, as plants will. In and in they are still creeping, surrounding the open water and making that area smaller and smaller. One day they will meet and there will be no more visible pond. But remember, as you walk on the sphagnum moss—the aquatic plant that forms the mat where other plants grow—that there is water underneath. You will be on a sort of floating mattress. Pick your footing carefully and walk where the moss is thickest and darkest. We'll show you," and he led the way down the hill through a strip of damp woods where royal ferns raised their handsome fronds, clintonia began to form its bright blue berries, and a carpet of goldthread lay underfoot. Poison sumac was noted and warned against. Graceful larches pointed upward. And as the campers drew near the water, a great blue heron flapped off over their heads with deliberate, measured wing beats.

They emerged at last into the full glare of the bog, and Jenny understood why they had been urged to wear hats. And also boots, because now they sank in to their ankles, and some of them even deeper, in the feathery yellow-green moss called sphagnum, that, Mr. Dillon had to remind them again, was really an unstable raft growing on water.

Jenny saw at once what David had meant by the trees quaking. If you moved a step, the bush ahead of you would quiver. If you actually jumped, trees five feet away started to shake. It was fun to jump and see the branches go up and down.

Some of the boys and girls were already wet from falling through the thin places. Brian was so interested in it all that he didn't care how wet he became. Jill, on the other hand, stayed very close to the roots of big trees, and Jenny resolved to remain as dry as possible while still having fun making things quake. Acting like a veteran of many such trips, David went around examining everything. Like Brian, he didn't seem to mind if he slipped through to his knees once in a while. "Mr. Dillon was sure right about that micro-climate," he'd say then, laughing.

In the bog pond white water lilies were in bloom. Gauzy-winged dragonflies with turquoise heads and iridescent emerald bodies, and steely-blue damsel flies hung suspended and then fled. "One way of telling them apart," Dan said, "is that dragonflies hold their wings straight out when at rest, and damsel flies fold theirs up and down, or at an angle. Dragonflies," he added, "are thought to be among our oldest land animals. Once they had wings two feet across."

Rosalie was calling the campers to where she stood on a small hummock near the water's edge. "Perhaps the most interesting of all bog life," she told them, "are the flowers that are believed to eat insects. For once, the plants turn the tables on them. This delicate little sundew catches insects in much the same way that flypaper does, by stickiness. Tiny hairs on the leaves that you can see sparkling with a gluey

liquid, as though with dew, hold fast to the prey while the plant dissolves and digests it."

Jenny, though sorry for the insects as she was always sorry for the flies on flypaper, thought just the same that the rosy, glistening sundews were very pretty and very well named. The leaves were indeed like little dew-drenched suns, the ones drawn on old maps with the round face and the rays going out.

"This showy pitcher plant," Rosalie went on, "has hollow, vase-like leaves that become filled with water after a rain. Insects found in these rain-filled pitchers seem to have difficulty getting out again because of the hairs within the leaves. You can feel these with your fingers. When the insects are drowned it is thought that they are absorbed by the plant as food."

The pitcher plant had a dark reddish-purple flower nodding on a gracefully arched stem surrounded by yellow-green leaves which fanned out in a whorl. Some of last year's dried pitchers remained, and the children picked them to take home. "I was told," Rosalie said, "that these special plants, which seem to be found only in acid, bog-like places, need the kind of nourishment they receive from insects because of the acute shortage of nitrogen in bogs."

Then she showed them other plants belonging to this habitat: the fragrant Labrador tea, with its rolled-over leaves lined beneath with a brownish substance like wool; the shrub, leather leaf; sweet gale; bog rosemary; the fairy-like dwarf cranberry; the dainty yellow-blossomed bladderwort that also captures insects; and sheep laurel with its magenta flowers. "Sheep laurel," Rosalie added, "is sometimes called lamb-kill, because of a belief that it is fatal to young stock. In Nova Scotia I've heard it called 'lamp-poison.' That shows how names and their meanings can get twisted about when they are only heard spoken."

Cedar waxwings peered down with their learned look from the black spruces and white cedars that, with the larches, surrounded the bog. A swamp sparrow chipped and trilled from a low bush. Redwings walked on the lily pads, and a chestnut-sided warbler was singing behind them halfway up the hill. "That bird has two distinctly different songs," David was telling Brian, "but the tone always seems to me to be the same."

"Here's an orchid!" Rosalie called then, and there was a great scramble to see it, and Jill got wet at last. Rosalie was pointing to the slight but exquisite white-fringed orchis of the eastern bogs and swamps. "That little thing?" demanded Jill, disappointed. "I'd never know that was an orchid."

"Lovelier here in its natural setting than anything in a florist's box, *I* think," Rosalie said, and Jenny, agreeing with her, asked, "May I have it, after everyone's had a look?"

"Keep the memory of it instead," Rosalie told her. "Then it will be always fresh and growing for you, instead of a dry brown stalk in a week or two. I think you'll be much happier with that. Our lady's-slippers are orchids too, and so is the arethusa. If these are picked the whole species suffers in its effort to survive. When I come upon them I clasp my hands safely behind my back, take a long look, and then walk quickly on. Let's collect all our native orchids that way."

Now the sun blazed down from its noon height, and Mr. Dillon was preparing to leave. "Bogs," he said, gathering together his equipment—binoculars, plant press, mason jars, and insect net, "are highly acid, and anything growing in one must therefore be able to thrive in acid conditions. This has always been true of bog plants, and can you guess how we know that? It's by means of one of the tiniest things you can think of, a grain of pollen. Pollen grains last for thousands of years. Scientists bore deep down into the peat bottom and, in the grains they find embedded there, observe what flourished in that spot centuries before."

Brian and David were reluctant to leave the bog; they would gladly have stayed all day. "Wasn't that great?" David asked. "It sure was," Brian agreed. "Toby would have enjoyed it too," he added, "I know he would." He was sorry now that his cousin had left. "I can't help feeling," he told Dan, who joined them then, "that somehow I could have prevented it. If I'd done more things with him——"

"You did quite enough with him," Dan reminded him. "And besides, I think his mind was made up before he came to camp not to like it. We've had boys of that sort here before. Occasionally they do come around, but often they don't. If someone has no feeling for nature, it's hard to make him happy at Greenwood."

"You did all you could, Brian," David told him. "He just missed baseball too much."

"If everyone was interested in studying nature all summer," Dan asked, "how could there ever be any World Series?"

When they returned they found a bottle of beer on the
workshop porch. "That's a strange thing to see at Greenwood," Rosalie remarked.

"It's for the mothing tonight," Dan told her. "A moth hunt,
like the butterfly hunt," he informed the campers, and they
all watched as Mr. Dillon mixed in a large tin can the beer,
which had been opened and was now stale, molasses, brown
sugar, honey, and some overripe raspberries, peaches, and
bananas.

"Ugh," said Jill, "who'd like that?"

But Jenny thought it smelled rather nice in an odd, sweet-
ish way. And she wondered, as she watched some of the boys
paint it onto the tree trunks with big brushes, if the moths
would think so too.

Later that evening, when the campers filled the woods
with their glowing flashlights like a whole swarm of fireflies
this time, and went back to examine the painted trees, they
found the pale moths all around them. They were like the
ghosts of butterflies, Jenny thought, as they clung to the
trunks where the syrup was, or fluttered about the branches,

103

or traveled right down the beams of light. Some were darker and had fantastic patterns on their wings, and such marvelous names as Io, Promethea, and Polyphemus. There were sphinx moths, hawk moths, and underwings with black and pink bands, and Brian saw the great Cecropia with its subtle shades of beige and coral and brown.

But it was on her way back to her tent that the most wonderful thing happened to Jenny. Out of a nearby tree a large pale-green shape came floating past her face. It had tapering swallowtail-like hind wings, with a transparent eyespot on each one. And she had no idea what it was. It did not act like a butterfly, and surely no moth could be so beautiful. In its fragile grace it had seemed almost unearthly; afterwards she couldn't be quite sure she had really seen it. But when she described it, Rosalie knew at once what it was. "A Luna moth!" she exclaimed, delighted too. "It's named for the moon, and it has been called the most beautiful insect in the world."

And Jenny could well believe this was true.

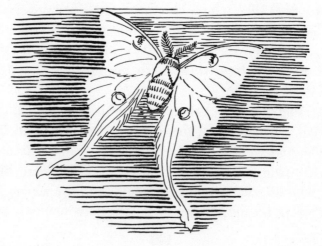

CHAPTER TEN

VISITING DAY AND STARS

WITH A flurry of activity Camp Greenwood prepared for visiting day. Tents were inspected morning and afternoon; the dining hall was decorated with wildflowers; exhibits in the workshop were arranged and then arranged again. Mr. Dillon went around with a preoccupied look, and the counselors flitted here and there like nervous butterflies.

Visiting day came on a Sunday halfway through the month. Two weeks ago the campers had arrived; two weeks from now some would have to leave. It scarcely seemed possible to Brian and Jenny.

"I wish time would start slowing up a little," said Brian. "Instead, it goes faster and faster."

"Yes," David agreed, "that's always the way it seems, especially here." He was pulling the blanket on his cot so tight that it lay without a wrinkle.

"This visiting day's really an interruption," pointed out Brian, who would have objected to anything that kept them from field trips and nature study.

105

"You'll be glad to see your parents though."

"Oh, I can always see them at home. Your family coming?"

"I wish they were," David said. He did not mind admitting he missed them. "But we live too far away."

At breakfast Mr. Dillon had announced that this was St. Swithin's Day. "There's a saying that if it rains on St. Swithin's Day, it will rain for the next forty. But weatherwise people like Greenwood campers know better than to believe in such fables." And anyway, thought Jenny, there isn't a cloud in sight.

She went down to Purple Finch to see Rosalie, and found Jill, who was supposed to be straightening up her bed, lying instead in the middle of it. "What's wrong?" Jenny asked.

"I was just thinking that camp's half over, and soon we'll be on the Cape again. Oh, I can hardly wait. I hope the time flies."

"It will," said Jenny. "But I wish it wouldn't."

"Are you coming to stay with us this August as usual?"

"I don't know. I suppose we probably shall." She said it without her usual tact or enthusiasm. She was thinking how much more she would prefer to stay at Greenwood. It was not possible this year, she realized, but, she kept telling herself hopefully, perhaps next summer.

When Brian's and Jenny's parents arrived, Brillig, the German shepherd, was with them. This was a complete and joyous surprise to both children, who hadn't realized how much they had missed their dog. And Brillig, from the way he bounded up on them, must have missed them just as much. "What a wonderful animal," David said, patting him too. "I'd like one just like him." And Jenny thought, if it were any dog but Brillig, how glad we'd be to let David have him.

Brian and Jenny had another surprise when they saw Cousin Laura, who had come to visit Jill, and Toby, who had simply come to visit. "Are you going to stay?" Brian wanted to know at once.

"Not on your life," Toby assured him. "That's the only reason I came back today, because I knew I didn't have to stay." And this, his cousin thought, was typical of Toby, who, even more than most boys, seemed to dislike being told what to do.

The workshop shone with a slightly unnatural spotlessness and looked oddly sedate with the chairs placed neatly in rows, and the insect nets all branching like a giant plant out of a piece of pipe, instead of being strewn about on shelves and tables. Greenwood's workshop was the chief attraction on visiting day. Mr. Dillon seemed very proud of it. He showed Mr. and Mrs. Vogel their son's birds' nest map. "Oh, he's keen on birds, all right," Brian's father said.

"But," the camp director told them, "he seems to be taking an interest in other things as well. *Most* other things," he added, smiling.

Cousin Laura was particularly pleased with the wildflower bouquets arranged by the campers themselves in such suitably simple containers as large glass jars, ironstone pitchers, and earthenware bean pots. "We found an orchid too, but Rosalie wouldn't let us pick it," Jill said. "It wasn't much of an orchid though," she went on, thinking of the ones worn by her favorite film stars.

It was beautiful, thought Jenny. "This is our plant parade," she said, running her finger along the table. Everything appeared perfect and fresh, from the bit of pond scum floating in a saucer to the composite daisy in a milk bottle. Only one or two specimens had had to be replaced before the visitors arrived. "This is what we were doing the day Toby ran off," Jill announced, still seeming almost proud of what her brother had done.

But her mother looked distressed then. "Oh, Mr. Dillon," she said later, "Greenwood seems like such a splendid camp, just the right one to rouse a child's interest in nature. I can't understand Toby really. In a way I think it must be my fault. Perhaps I was too anxious for him, and urged him too hard. His father would probably have succeeded where I seem to have failed."

"I'm sorry I didn't know about Toby's father," Mr. Dillon told her. "I might have handled things a little differently. Any mistake that was made is as much mine as yours."

Cousin Laura sighed. "Mr. Dillon, I have absolutely no criticism of you or your camp. Everything that I've seen and heard has been excellent." She called to Rosalie then and suggested that they take a short walk together. "I want to talk to you about several things," she said.

"Jenny, are you happy here?" her mother asked anxiously, as Jenny stood, a little wilted, watching Cousin Laura and Rosalie leave the workshop and go down along the trail, talking earnestly and, no doubt, about Jill.

Almost happy, she might have answered then, but she said instead, "Oh, Greenwood is a wonderful place. Who wouldn't be happy here!"

"Jenny knows the different bird songs," David told her parents. "She's helped me with some I hadn't learned before."

"I haven't helped much," Jenny said. Not as much as I'd like to, she thought, patting Brillig, who licked her hand gratefully.

"David must come to visit us at home sometime," Mrs.

Vogel suggested, and, "Oh, yes!" agreed Jenny. And Brian added, "Or when we go to Cousin Laura's."

"I like the seashore," David volunteered, but Brian was thinking of Cousin Laura's farm in Maryland.

"I guess we don't have to ask you whether you're enjoying yourself, do we, Brian?"

Brian shook his head a bit brusquely, looking embarrassed. Parents, he sometimes thought, might have the best and kindest instincts in the world, but they could often make one feel the most awkward. He had been glad to see them, and overjoyed to see Brillig, but now he couldn't help wishing that all the families and friends would go home so the camp could return to normal.

In the chapel in the woods, which was really row upon row of logs arranged in a semicircle around a pine needle clearing, Dan Alderman led a short vesper service. The campers participated too. Brian read his favorite psalm:

"'I will lift up mine eyes unto the hills; from whence cometh
    my help?
My help cometh from the Lord, who hath made heaven
    and earth. . . .'"

He did not really have to read it, he knew it by heart, but for some reason he did not like to admit this. David played a flute solo from an air in the *Pastoral Symphony*, and Jenny's contribution was a poem by Van Dyke called "The Veery." She had found it in the camp library.

"'. . . But far away, and far away, the tawny thrush is singing;
New England woods, at close of day, with that clear chant are ringing. . . .'"

The thrushes were indeed singing: the hermit with its distant, eloquent evensong; the wood thrush, the voice of the forest, it seemed, at Greenwood; and robins too in liquid joy. A purple finch joined in. Golden light from the sinking sun fell in gently brilliant arches between the trees. Cousin Laura, sitting with her children and Rosalie, dabbed quickly at her eyes. And Toby, always disturbed by grownups' tears, thought to himself that mothers seemed to cry almost as much as sisters.

"Your family's really great," David told Brian when everyone had left.

"Yes, they really are," agreed Brian. Now that they had gone he regretted that he had not seemed more enthusiastic about their visit. But this was the way it always was, and he imagined they understood.

The evening was warm and cloudless; the moon had not yet risen. "I think," Mr. Dillon proposed, "this would be a fine night for star study."

Jenny almost clapped her hands she was so delighted. For she had been looking forward to this. And Brian was always pleased by anything that kept them up beyond the usual camp bedtime. "I like the stars," David said. "When you're alone at night it's nice to know they're there."

The campers gathered by the pond, where the tranquil water reflected the constellations overhead, making them look as though they floated on the still surface.

"Stars, as you know, are really suns," Mr. Dillon began, "like *our* sun, only much farther away. They shine by their own light. And they are moving, though you and I would probably never know this if we weren't told."

Brian said, "I thought it was the earth moving that made the stars *seem* to move."

"Quite so," agreed the camp director. "The rotation of the earth *does* make the stars appear to rise in the east, cross the heavens, and set in the west, when all the time we know it is *we* who are being moved past *them*. But stars also have motions of their own, altogether apart from this other effect. Arcturus, for instance, that bright one toward the west, is actually whirling through space at the rate of eighty-four miles per second. But there's no need to concern yourselves with such figures tonight."

And Jenny was thankful for this because thinking of speeds like eighty-four miles a second made her feel rather dizzy. Brian, on the other hand, thought he would enjoy going that fast. It would certainly make it a lot quicker getting from one place to another, though he doubted if he would see much on the way.

"Let's look up now," Mr. Dillon suggested, and they all tilted back their heads. "The summer sky brings us, for one thing, the impressive beauty of the Milky Way. Do you see it slanting down toward the horizon like a luminous scarf? It's made up of billions of stars. I like to think of our universe as resembling a sheet of paper, with our earth a dot on this sheet. When we look up into most of the sky we are looking out from the paper. But when we stare into the Milky Way we are peering through the *length* of the paper to the very edge. And all around us is black, soundless space."

Jill's neck was becoming stiff from looking up, and she said so.

"Then let's lie down," Mr. Dillon suggested. "The grass is still dry. This is the best way to look at the heavens, the way the Arabs, who named many stars and constellations, must have lain at night on the warm sands.

"It's very satisfying to be able to call some of the stars by name. Unlike birds and insects, and even wildflowers and trees, wherever you go in this latitude the star patterns will remain the same. In the middle of Paris or on the Gobi Desert you will see the very ones that you see here.

"Above us now is Vega, the brightest star in the summer skies. Winter's brightest, and the brightest of all, is Sirius, the Dog Star, that follows at the heels of the hunter Orion. Arcturus ranks fourth."

Mr. Dillon then showed them the North, or Pole, Star, with the Big and Little Dippers always swung so that they appear to empty into one another; the great W of Cassiopeia's

113

chair; lovely semicircular Corona Borealis, the Crown of the North; Hercules; and what he called his favorite, Cygnus, the Swan, flying down the Milky Way with the bright star Deneb for its tail. Seeing its graceful long neck and wing-spread, Jenny decided that this constellation, also known as the Northern Cross, was her favorite too.

Brian's was Aquila, the Eagle, with brilliant Altair in the center, and Jill liked Delphinus, the Dolphin, shaped like a kite. Rosalie showed them the visible Zodiac signs, believed by some to shape the destinies of those born under them— the Lion, setting, with pale-blue Regulus; the Virgin; the Scales; and the Scorpion with red Antares blazing forth in it.

"Constellations are groups of stars that men's imaginations have put together because of their resemblance to earthly ob-jects or mythological beings. Some of us have a difficult time seeing these resemblances, and some see other things that are not drawn as such on the charts. For me there is a camel climbing near the end of the Milky Way, but you won't find him mentioned in astronomy books. Perhaps the Arabs saw enough camels during the daytime.

"When you are lying this way," Mr. Dillon said finally, for they stayed there, reluctant to put even the shelter of tents and pine trees between them and the stars, "you probably think that you are looking up into the sky. Now think of the earth as an orange to which you are held by gravity, and turn the orange over, as the earth turns every day. You are still lying on your back, but you are looking *down*."

"Down?" wondered Brian.

"You are hanging on the underside of the orange, or of the

world, looking down into the far reaches of space. Isn't it more exciting to think of it that way?"

Jenny sat up and squirmed uncomfortably. It might be more exciting that way, but it gave her the uneasy feeling that she could fall off and out and down forever. She imagined herself tumbling past the warm brightness of all those suns. I guess I'd better be sure to stay on the top of the orange, she thought.

"What's the matter, Jenny?" asked Rosalie.

"The stars make me feel so small and unimportant," she said, hesitant to share her fantasy, voicing instead a universal feeling that mankind has always known.

Mr. Dillon put his hand gently on her head.

> " 'Though compared with a star
>   You are only a dot,
>   You can think and love,
>   And a star cannot.'

"And that will always be true of every one of us," he added, bidding them good night.

CHAPTER ELEVEN

A SUMMING-UP, NATURE TRAILS,
AND A THUNDERSTORM

Now FOR Brian and Jenny and Jill their days at camp were almost over. David was going to stay another month. "Isn't there any way you could manage it too?" he asked his friends hopefully.

"If there were," Brian told him, "I'd have thought of it and done something about it before this." He kicked his heel disconsolately against the tent platform. "The rest of the summer will seem pretty dull." He had forgotten how he had looked forward to the freedom of roaming through the woods and fields.

"No, it won't," David was saying. "You'll be able to put into use all the things you've learned here. The time between now and when school starts should be the best you've ever had."

This was the best I ever had, thought Brian, watching the vibrations of a wood thrush's throat as it sang not ten feet away.

116

In the workshop where they had become so accustomed to gathering after breakfast, Mr. Dillon was waiting. "We have studied many things separately," he began; "birds, trees, insects, and so on. But don't ever forget that I want you to keep putting all these together in your minds, so that you'll have before you wherever you go the picture of life as a *whole,* with its countless interrelationships and dependencies. Many creatures, birds for instance, may seem to live to themselves, but this is not the case. They are very much a part of their environment, affected by weather, plant life, food supply, and predators. And this has been true since the first one appeared on earth a hundred and fifty million years ago."

"Which bird was that?" asked Brian.

"It has been called archaeopteryx, which means 'ancient wing.' It was slightly smaller than a crow and had a very long tail. And what color do you suppose it was?"

"Black," said Brian, the crow making him think of it.

"Blue," guessed Jenny, reminded of a bluejay.

Mr. Dillon smiled. "That was an unfair question of mine," he admitted. "Actually we have no idea what color it was. You may imagine it any or all shades of the rainbow. We only know about the archaeopteryx at all because of fossils that were found."

Someone asked him then to tell them about fossils.

"Fossils are really casts, like the wax or plaster casts that you make of animal tracks. Early in the history of the world, a bit of fern, an insect, or an archaeopteryx fell into mud and slowly decayed, leaving its imprint. The mud hardened, and other mud or solutions washed into the print, and these too hardened and eventually, perhaps under the weight and pressure of the sea, turned into rock. Years and years later, when the rock was split apart, there on one side was the imprint and on the other the raised cast. So in fossils we read the story of the life of long ago."

"Are they hard to find?" David inquired.

"I'm afraid I can't answer that," Mr. Dillon told him, "because I've never found one or known anybody who did. But people who understand how and where to look must not have too much difficulty because I do know that some fossils are not at all expensive to buy, considering they are antiques that are really antique. You might start a fossil collection. There is an indescribable thrill in holding in one's hand the mold of something that lived during the Age of the Reptiles.

"Well," he concluded then, "you have learned something about nature's beginnings, the first plants and animals coming out of water—the source of life—to survive on land and commence a pattern that was followed by forests of ferns and club mosses, and a succession of dinosaurs which proceeded to flourish and then disappear forever. You have seen how the warm-blooded mammals developed into the leaders of the animal world, as our trees became the giants of the plant kingdom. But always bear in mind that there is still a constant struggle for supremacy and even for existence. Trees race to beat one another up into the light; the ones that cannot make it often die. Animals in their never-ending hunger are also struggling to keep alive. The shrew eats the newt and the owl eats the shrew.

"But," he went on, seeing the dismay on the faces of some of them, "you must not be upset by this. Nature manages a

118

delicate and fine balance, which man is not needed to help maintain. Nature could get along just as well without us. Long ago it *did*."

This was an awesome thought to Jenny. Though we could not live without nature, it could get along without us. And it did not make her feel insignificant, but rather filled her with a new respect and admiration for the world around her.

"There's just one more thing I want you to be thinking about," Mr. Dillon told them, "and that is that nothing in the present is final or finished. Everything continues and goes on. Changes are always under way. You may not see any in your lifetime, but if you'd lived in the Coal Age you might not have seen any either. The world as we know it is up-to-date, and the past is complete; every minute completes it. But this moment and the future and life itself are like a great river running over the land, a river that does not cease and that slowly and imperceptibly causes minute alterations which in time grow into developments as important as the first liverwort or amphibian gaining the shore."

Dan met them in the clearing. He was carrying a small saw and some other tools. "This looks as if I'm planning to put you to work, doesn't it? And I am, though maybe not this afternoon." He laid the tools down carefully in front of them. "I painted all the handles red," he pointed out. "Any idea why?"

"So you could spot them easily," David said.

"Right," Dan told him. "If I'm working in the woods and put my saw down in a hurry because I see a salamander or something, I can find the saw again later without too much trouble."

"How did you know that?" Brian asked David.

"It's the same reason that they make stop lights red, to attract your attention."

"Of course," Dan was saying, "it's always better *not* to put your tools down in a hurry, whatever color they're painted.

For one thing, if they're sharp as good tools ought to be, they shouldn't be dropped because they might fall on you, or somebody else; and for another thing, if they're mislaid even for one night, that's just the time it'll rain and you may have a problem with rust."

"What does all this have to do with nature?" Jill wanted to know. Because Jill thought she knew Dan well, Jenny surmised, she believed she could say anything to him that she wanted to. Jenny herself would not have asked such a question.

But Dan didn't seem to mind. "All right," he said agreeably, "I'll try to tell you. First of all, how many of you think you've learned something here this month?"

Everyone raised a hand, and Jenny would like to have raised two.

"Now what do you plan to do with it?"

Do with it? wondered Brian.

"I mean, would you like to share it with somebody else? Most of us would, I think. I do, that's why I teach here in the summer. I know you can't instruct a class yet, but there's another way that you can share the things you've learned at Greenwood. What I have in mind is a nature trail."

"Are we going to make one?" David asked with interest.

"I hope," Dan said, "that many of you will want to make one, not here, but around your own homes or schools, where others can enjoy it too. That's why I brought these tools out, to show you what you will need. You probably have most of them already in your garages or basements.

"A small saw is exceedingly useful, and you won't need a larger one. If a big tree is in your way, let your path go around it. That's one of the advantages of a nature trail. It can and should wind wherever you want it to. You aren't building a straight highway, or interested, fortunately, in the shortest distance between two points.

"Clippers are handy for small branches and shoots and vines. And these long-handled clippers, called loppers, are good for higher branches and thicker ones. But I have made a perfectly adequate trail with only a small saw and a pair of clippers."

"What about an axe?" inquired Brian.

"Axes and hatchets," Dan told him, "are the tools of the experienced woodsman, not of the young camper, even a Greenwood camper. I shan't be there to watch you when you're making your trails, and I don't want to think of you swinging axes or hatchets around for the first time by yourselves. I assume you understand that *all* cutting instruments can be dangerous if not handled correctly and kept in good condition. It's the blunt knife, you know, that causes the trouble."

He showed them then how to saw small trees as close to the ground as possible to prevent stumps in the trail that might trip someone. He also showed how to cut a branch off close along a trunk so that no ends protruded, and how to clip at such an angle that the cut surface would face away from the trail and be out of sight.

"A nature trail," he went on, "should not be too long, and it should have a place to stop and rest, with a boulder or tree trunk for a seat, and perhaps a view. It should be winding, and only wide enough for walking comfortably single-file. And it should end not far from the beginning; you can make a sort of loop. It goes without saying that it should pass as many interesting natural objects as possible. These can include a variety of trees and shrubs, wildflowers, and lower plants like ferns, lichens, mosses, and mushrooms, even though these last may not appear the next year. You can always say on the marker that inky-cap mushrooms have been found in this spot, and that an ovenbird or vireo once nested nearby. All these additions increase the variety and value of the trail."

Then he explained how to make weatherproof wooden and metal markers, and offered suggestions about what to put on them. "Don't just state 'red oak' or 'white pine.' Remember that you're giving your friends a chance to take a field trip any time they can, without having to rely on a leader. Let your signs speak for you, and tell something interesting about what's being observed. And remember also three words in connection with your nature trail: naturalness, simplicity, and conservation. Naturalness because after all it is a *nature* trail. Simplicity because your friends may not know as much about the out-of-doors as you do. And conservation because you, and everyone at Greenwood, are first and foremost conservationists. Teach and practice conservation, the preserving and wise use of natural resources, and the world will look and *be* better because of you."

Brian hoped Mr. Crandall would be interested in making a nature trail at school for one of their science projects. And Jenny thought that she would like to have a trail in their woods at home. I'll call it the Greenwood trail, she said to herself, and mark on it all the things I've learned about and seen at camp.

The day, sultry from the beginning, had become hot and oppressive. Tree frogs trilled. The still afternoon air weighed down on them, and in the west thunder began to rumble. "Oh dear," murmured Jenny apprehensively.

"Close your eyes during the storm," David told her. "You won't mind it so much that way."

In Partridgeberry the girls fastened their tent flaps in preparation for the rain that seemed just about to come. They could smell it in the air that moved now through the forest. Everything was very dark; inside the tent it was almost like night. Jenny sat still and firm in the middle of her cot, her eyes tight shut.

Then she heard Rosalie's voice. "Why don't you all go down to Purple Finch," she was suggesting. "It's bigger, and you'll have the others for company. I'll be along as soon as I've checked these flaps."

"I'll wait for you," Jenny said at once, and even as she spoke the rain poured down. It fell like a curtain between them and the trees. As though from far away she heard the squeals of the girls dashing to reach the shelter of the larger tent. "I guess," Rosalie told her, "we have no choice now but to wait here till it lets up."

Jenny went back to sit on her cot, and Rosalie sat on the one next to hers. "Did Jill tell you I was afraid of thunderstorms?" Jenny asked, and Rosalie acknowledged that she had. "I suppose *she* isn't afraid of anything," Jenny remarked a little enviously.

"Oh, I guess all of us have things that worry us from time to time," Rosalie told her, "most of them needlessly, as it turns out. Like Mrs. Ashton and Jill's homesickness."

Jenny was scarcely aware of the thunder resounding outside, or of the lightning that flashed beyond the corners of
the tent where the wind lifted them. "What," she asked,
absorbed, "about Jill's homesickness?"

And Rosalie told her then that her Cousin Laura had been
concerned about the possibility of her daughter's being
homesick at Greenwood, and that she had urged her to look
after Jill, and be with her as much as possible. She had even
asked her to assign Jill a bed near hers. The reason for their
apparent friendship suddenly became clear to Jenny. "Mrs.
Ashton told me that I wouldn't have to worry about you at
all. She said that even though you were younger than Jill,
you were much more self-sufficient and adaptable, and more
likely to enjoy camp."

"Did she ask you to write to me last spring?"

"Yes, and I'm glad she did."

The rain pelted down upon the tent, but Jenny hardly

heard it. Still thinking about Jill, she said, "Is that why she acts so grown-up sometimes, because she really isn't, or doesn't feel she is?"

"Don't you think that's often the case?" replied Rosalie.

She made Jenny feel adult and wise. It's because she doesn't treat me like a child, she thought, gratified. "I'd figured out that you and Jill must be very close friends at school," she admitted then.

"Goodness, no," Rosalie said, "she's much younger than I am. I was only doing what her mother wanted me to. I like her mother very much."

So do I, thought Jenny, and she had to ask, "Do you like me too?"

Rosalie smiled. "Counselors aren't supposed to have favorite campers," she said, "but if we were, it would be hard for me not to choose you."

At supper that night Jenny sat beside David. "This is Jenny," she told him.

"I thought so. I can tell your walk. It's good fun to know people by their walks; it's a game I play with myself quite often. Well," he added, "it wasn't such a bad storm, was it?"

And, "No," Jenny agreed enthusiastically, "I even enjoyed it."

CHAPTER TWELVE

THE GREENWOOD CAMPFIRE

"Brian," Dan began, assuming a severe look, "Mr. Dillon wants to see you in his office right away."

"Oh, gosh," said Brian with misgivings, and his expression asked, What do you suppose I've done now?

"With your binoculars," Dan added, breaking into a grin, and Brian almost ran from his tent to where the camp director was waiting.

"We've talked about a bird walk for a long time," Mr. Dillon told him, "and this morning I decided it's now or never. At the beginning of each session you think there'll be so much time to get everything done. Then suddenly it's flown by. But you can say that about every day, can't you?"

They went back to the tall spruces where once they had talked about forests and heard the Blackburnian warbler. "And there he is!" Mr. Dillon exclaimed, and at last Brian saw through his glasses the brilliant "fire-throat." As it moved against the dark green branches it reminded him of a candle flame on a Christmas tree. "I couldn't let you leave camp," the director said, "without a sight of this bird that is so typical of Greenwood Forest."

"Is it the most beautiful warbler of all?" asked Brian, quite ready to believe it was.

Mr. Dillon replied, "Ask ten different people what the most beautiful warbler is, and you'll get ten different answers. There'd certainly be votes for the redstart and the cerulean, the prothonotary and the bay-breasted, the black-throated blue, parula, Cape May, golden-winged, and just as many more. My own favorite is the black-throated green, but I couldn't tell you just why. People have their own particular reasons for liking certain birds. Sometimes they don't know why themselves."

"Cousin Laura says she likes the whip-poor-will because it reminds her of her childhood."

"Perhaps you'll like the Blackburnian because it reminds you of Greenwood."

Through the branches then came the song that Brian had heard the afternoon he arrived at camp. "There," he cried, "that, whatever it is, is the bird that will remind me of Greenwood. It was the first one I heard here."

"The blue-headed vireo," Mr. Dillon told him, "that nests where the evergreens are joined by other trees. Is it a new bird for you? Come then, you must see him." And in a few moments Brian had spotted this handsome vireo with its "spectacles" and pearl-white breast, and heard it sing again its ringing, slurring phrases. "The first vireo to arrive in the spring," Mr. Dillon said, "and a good sign that cold weather is over.

"Brian," he went on as they walked back through the woods, "sometimes we have boys here at camp that we watch with special interest. Not necessarily because they're brighter or more enthusiastic about nature than other boys, but because a combination of aptitude and manner and alertness makes us feel that they may one day become good counselors. You are still quite young, and need to develop a sense of responsibility and self-discipline, but I believe that all the right material is there. I hope very much that you will be back for the entire summer next year. I could arrange a scholarship for you if you wouldn't be able to come otherwise."

Brian hardly knew what to say. "Do you mean I'd be like Dan?" he asked at last, a bit breathless.

Mr. Dillon laughed and patted his shoulder. "We don't guarantee to turn out duplicates of Dan or any other counselors. We are more interested in you as an individual, and I'm sure you'll agree that's better for you too. But we would certainly hope that eventually you'd be able to do as much for young people as Dan and your friend Mr. Crandall do."

"Once," Brian told him happily, "I thought I wanted to be an ornithologist. Now I think I'd rather be a nature counselor than anything else."

"Well," concluded Mr. Dillon, pleased, "who knows, you may be both!"

Jenny finished her packing and then wondered what to do next. It was such a strange day. It had seemed unnatural not to meet in the workshop as usual; she was so used to the camp routine. Here I am, she thought, still at Greenwood and yet already missing it. What will it be like tomorrow and later on?

She wandered down to Purple Finch and found Rosalie busy helping Jill pack. Jill's clothes were spread out over two cots; she looked as though she did not know where to begin. "Why, hello, Jenny," Rosalie said, glad to see her, but Jenny realized at once that this was no time for a visit.

Then she saw David coming along the forest trail. He swung his stick in front of him to avoid any tree trunks that might block his way. And he walked with an easy stride and a look of pleasure. "The woods are beautiful today," he told Jenny as she joined him.

"Oh, yes," she agreed, "aren't they? But then they're always beautiful. I'm going to miss them so much, and camp, and—and all of you." She paused and sighed. "What do you do, David, when you feel sad?"

He considered this. "Well," he said at last, "I guess I don't feel sad very often, not that I can remember anyway. But if I do, I try to think about the way God must have planned the universe, and how He figured out nature so that every-thing works together and fits in so well. Even when He made the seasons He arranged for the animals and plants and the smallest insects to adjust themselves to the changes. And if I ever start feeling sorry for myself, I remember God's love which surrounds us like a circle of light; you know, Mr. Dillon told us about it that first evening. When you think of things like that it's just impossible to be un-happy."

"Oh, David," said Jenny, admiring him so much and wish-ing she could tell him. "You've made camp so special for me—you and Rosalie. And I'll remember what you said, and think about it when I'm missing people and things here."

They had come out of the woods into the clearing. Baby rabbits played on the damp grass; buttercups glistened. Wild raspberries ripened on their long canes. And a gleam of the purest blue flashed by. "Oh," Jenny gasped, "that must have been an indigo bunting! It was all blue, there was no other color on it. David," she asked, a little shyly, "have you any idea what blue looks like?"

"I know it must be pretty," he answered at once, "be-cause it's the shade of the sea and the sky."

"And your eyes," said Jenny, "and your shirt."

He said casually, "I never have any idea what I'm wear-

ing. I just reach for the nearest thing that's clean. Jenny," he continued, "why don't you let me know later if what I told you really does help you when you're sad."

She had forgotten all about being sad. "Could I write to you?" she asked. She hadn't thought of this before. "I mean, could you——?"

"I write a lot of letters," he told her. "I learned to type so I could. But my spelling's terrible."

"Oh," she exclaimed eagerly, "so's mine!" She could hardly have felt happier.

The campers sat in a circle around the great campfire. Up soared the flames with tiny bits of gold-dust brilliance circling round and out into the night. The sky and the shadows were like velvet all about them.

"'Gone to bed is the setting sun,
      Night is coming and day is done,
      Whip-poor-will, whip-poor-will, has just begun.'"

Rosalie led and they sang in unison, watching her hand
move back and forth against the stars.

Fireflies rose from the grass. "Did you know that fireflies have a secret?" Rosalie asked when the song was over.

"How could they have a secret?" Brian wondered.

"They have the secret of cold light, one that many humans would like to fathom. If you touch an electric bulb after it's been on for a while, it will feel hot. But nobody ever burned his hand catching fireflies."

The logs settled; glowing fragments broke and scattered. "Watch for the salamanders!" Dan cried, but though they watched intently they really knew that salamanders couldn't live in flames as legends said they did. Still it was fun to look for them and see all the other shapes in the fire, as changeful as clouds on a summer day.

"'If there were witchcraft,'" Mr. Dillon began; it was his favorite.

"'I'd make two wishes,'" they all sang then,
"'A winding road that beckons me to roam,
And then I'd wish for a blazing campfire,
To welcome me when I'm returning home.'"

Frogs in the darkening pond seemed to join in. And birds, usually quiet by this time, chirped now and then in the dusky foliage. A bat fluttered out over the clearing. Jill squealed and covered her hair, but the bat appeared interested only in the insects which it caught on the wing in its sudden darting flight.

Dan threw a pile of brush onto the fire and it roared up, whole leaves floating heavenwards, glowing and leaf-shaped still.

"'Rise up, O flame,'" began Rosalie, and in a round they

134

went on, "'Rise up, O rise up, O rise up, O flame,
    By thy light glowing,
    Show to us beauty,
    Vision, and joy.'"

Mr. Dillon stood before them, the firelight playing across his face. "We don't as a rule make awards until the end of the summer," he said. "But this camper will not be with us then. So I'm going to present now this volume of the *Birds of America* prints by John James Audubon to Brian Vogel for having discovered a new bird for Camp Greenwood, the Louisiana water thrush."

Everyone applauded, and Brian stood up slowly. How thrilled he must be, thought his sister, thrilled too.

But Brian was shaking his head. "I didn't find the bird," he told them; "Jenny did."

"Then the Vogels walk off with the birding honors," Mr. Dillon declared, "which is as it should be, since their name means 'bird.'"

And Rosalie turned around and smiled warmly at Jenny.

"But there're other things in nature besides birds," Brian was saying.

Hearing him, Jenny marveled. Already he was talking like Dan and Mr. Crandall. How grown-up her brother seemed suddenly, standing there with the camp director, accepting the book, and then bringing it around the circle of upturned heads to where she sat. "It's for you," he said, and strode off before she could murmur a word.

The counselors and old campers began the farewell song to the ones who were leaving,

> "Remember your Greenwood summer,
> Next winter, and all year through,
> Remember——"

Rosalie moved in between Jenny and Jill, her arms around their waists. Across the flames Jenny saw David with his alert look of interest in everything, and Brian, his wide eyes shining.

> "Remember the friends you made here,
> And all that you've learned to do;
> And please don't forget Camp Greenwood,
> For Greenwood remembers you."

Mr. Dillon picked up some small branches. One by one he tossed them onto the bonfire, and with each branch he said the name of a camper who was about to go. "Now," he told them, "you are a part of Greenwood forever, its woods, its light, its spirit."

David, standing very straight, played taps. "God is nigh," said Jenny, remembering the words, and what David had told her. And how true it was, she thought, that everything fell into place and fit so perfectly.

"Do you think you'll come back next year?" Jill asked Jenny as the girls started off toward their tents.

"Oh, I hope you will," said Rosalie.

Jenny looked behind her to where Brian and David and Dan were helping Mr. Dillon put out the campfire with his Indian pump. She watched their silhouettes against the glow of the flames, and then the fire died down to gray and coral embers, and it was too dark to see anyone. It's funny, she thought, I should be so proud and happy that Rosalie wants me to come back next year, and I am, of course, but right now I don't want to think about next year. I want to concentrate as hard as I can on *this* year, what it is and what it has meant, so that I don't lose even the tiniest part of it, ever.

"She's sleepy," Jill announced, when her cousin didn't answer.

But Rosalie slipped her hand into Jenny's. "I believe I understand," she said.

And to think, Jenny told herself, there was once a time when I wasn't even sure I wanted to come to Greenwood.

Her brother, raking over the wet-looking ground where so recently the flames had danced, was remembering the same thing. "Do you know, sir," he informed Mr. Dillon, "I almost didn't come to this camp. I thought I could learn more about nature on my own. It was Mr. Crandall who talked me into it."

Mr. Dillon smiled. "Indeed? And are you sorry you listened?"

Brian tried to answer this, but the only words he could think of to express his feeling about Greenwood seemed too sentimental. He was afraid they might laugh at him if he told them what an inspiring place he had found it.

"I guess Brian's shown how he feels about camp," Dan remarked. "And he says he's coming back next summer. He has to, to learn about butterflies and a few other subjects he missed this time."

"That's right," observed Mr. Dillon, "he did skip part of the program, didn't he?"

They could joke about it now, and even Brian could join in.

David put his hand on his friend's arm as they started down the trail. "I have a lot to learn about butterflies too," he told him.

"I have a lot to learn about *everything*," Brian declared. "This has really been just the beginning."

NOTES

TALK ABOUT THE WEATHER

Weather can be called the state of the air around us, air which is not simply oxygen, but 78% nitrogen, 21% oxygen, and 1% other gases including hydrogen, neon, and carbon dioxide.

Wind has been defined as air moving over the earth's surface. How can we tell how fast it moves? Here is a scale originated over one hundred and fifty years ago by Sir Francis Beaufort, a British admiral.

Beaufort number	*Speed (miles per hour)*	*Description*	*Observation*
0	less than 1	calm	smoke rises vertically
1	1-3	light air	smoke drifts slowly
2	4-7	slight breeze	leaves rustle
3	8-12	gentle breeze	leaves and twigs in constant motion
4	13-18	moderate breeze	dust, loose paper, small branches move
5	19-24	fresh breeze	small trees in leaf begin to sway
6	25-31	strong breeze	large branches in motion
7	32-38	moderate gale	whole trees in motion
8	39-46	fresh gale	twigs break off trees
9	47-54	strong gale	branches break, slight damage to houses
10	55-63	whole gale	trees snap and are uprooted
11	64-75	storm	widespread damage
12	above 75	hurricane	extreme danger and excessive damage

Clouds are advance messengers of the weather to come. They are grouped for us into four "families" according to their height in the sky.

High Clouds

Name	Appearance	Composition	Rain or Snow	Prediction
Cirrus	thin, wispy curls feathers "mares' tails"	ice	none	fair, but unsettled, changing weather if clouds thicken in west
Cirro-stratus	thin, gauzy veils "halos" around sun or moon	ice	none	rain probably coming before long
Cirro-cumulus	rippled sand wave-like flakes "mackerel sky"	ice	none	rain and warmer when thicker clouds follow

Middle Clouds

Name	Appearance	Composition	Rain or Snow	Prediction
Alto-stratus	thick ashy or blue-gray sheets	ice and water	steady rain or snow	usually bad weather and temperature change
Alto-cumulus	cottony balls in rows puffs and rolls "polka dots"	usually water	occasional light rain or snow	warm or cold front on the way

Low Clouds

Name	Appearance	Composition	Rain or Snow	Prediction
Strato-cumulus	gray puffy layer rolling waves	water	infrequent drizzle or snow flurries	fair or changing weather
Stratus	fog-like sheets leaden sky "high fog"	usually water	infrequent fine drizzle or snow	often clearing in the morning, but may turn into nimbostratus
Nimbo-stratus	dark, wet, low, torn, ragged sheets	ice and water	steady rain or snow	can bring long precipitation warmer weather follows

Towering Clouds

Name	Appearance	Composition	Rain or Snow	Prediction
Cumulus *	puffs of wool "fair weather clouds"	water	none	fair weather unless they become cumulonimbus
Cumulo-nimbus	heavy, cauliflower-shaped, often anvil-like form (cirrus) at top	ice and water	heavy showers rain or snow perhaps hail	thunder and lightning changing temperatures usually follow

---

* The snowy brightness of these clouds is caused by the tiny droplets of moisture which reflect the sun like miniature mirrors held up to it.

Some Weather Sayings

Usually reliable

When the dew is on the grass
Rain will seldom come to pass.

Red sky at night, sailors' delight;
Red sky at morning, sailors take warning.
Mackerel sky, soon wet or dry.

The higher the clouds,
The fairer the weather.

When the glass falls low
Prepare for a blow.

Rising waves mean rising winds.

When the wind is in the west,
That's the time we love the best.

When the wind is in the south,
Then the rain is in its mouth.

Rain before seven,
Clear before eleven.

A ring around the moon means rain.

When birds fly low
Fair skies will go.

If your hair crackles when you comb it,
the air is relatively dry.

Static on the radio means a
thunderstorm nearby.

In the morning mountains
(towering clouds),
In the evening fountains
(thunderstorms).

The moon and the weather may change
together,
But a change in the moon does not
change the weather.

Mostly unreliable

If the groundhog sees its
shadow on the second of February, prepare for six more
weeks of winter.

Bushy woolly bear caterpillars, squirrel tails, and cattails; numerous skunks, blue
jays, squirrels, etc.; wild geese
and other birds flying south
early, etc., etc. foretell a severe
winter.

Any cat with rising tail
Indicates approaching gale.

A change in the moon (or the
tide) means a change in the
weather.

The sun crossing the Equinox
brings a storm with it.

Rain on St. Swithin's Day
means rain for the next
forty.

A new moon turned on its back
holds rain.

Lightning never strikes twice
in the same place.

141

Read about the Weather. Here are some books for further weather reading: *

All About the Weather. Ivan Ray Tannehill. Random House, Inc., New York.

Eric Sloane's Weather Book. Eric Sloane. Little, Brown & Company, Boston.

Everyday Weather and How It Works. Herman Schneider. McGraw-Hill Book Company, New York.

Guest Weathercaster. Raymond M. Sager. Guest Products Corporation, New York.

How to Know and Predict the Weather. Robert Moore Fisher. New American Library, New York.

1001 Questions Answered about the Weather. Frank H. Forrester. Dodd, Mead & Company, New York.

Understanding the Weather. T. M. Longstreth. The Macmillan Company, New York.

Weather. Paul E. Lehr, R. Will Burnett, and Herbert S. Zim. Simon and Schuster, Inc., New York.

Weather Handbook. Lou Williams. Girl Scouts of U.S.A., New York.

Why the Weather? C. F. Brooks. Harcourt, Brace & Company, New York.

KNOW THE TREES

Seven Questions to Ask and Answer.
1. Is it a *tree?*

   A single woody stem or trunk is usually the clue to this one.
2. Has it *leaves* or *needles?*
3. If it has *needles,*
   A. Are the needles in *bundles?*

      Five needles in bundle = *White Pine*

      Three needles in bundle = *Pitch Pine*

      Two needles in bundle = *Red Pine, Jack Pine, Scotch Pine* or *Austrian Pine*
   B. Are the needles in *tufts?* = *Larch*
   C. Are the needles *single* (separate)?

      Needles four-sided, sharply pointed, roll easily between the

---

* Throughout these notes some of the volumes recommended will be found most suitable for the youngest readers of *Greenwood Summer*. Many are for the most advanced. Because of the differences in individuals, it is difficult to generalize according to age groups. I suggest that wherever possible the books be examined before buying.

fingers, grow at random on the branch, and leave the twig rough when bare = *Spruce*

Needles fragrant, flattish, grow in parallel rows, and leave the twig smooth when bare = *Fir*

Needles shorter (½″ long), soft to touch, grow on opposite sides of the twig like the veins of a feather, and have twin white lines underneath = *Hemlock*

    D. Do the needles *overlap* like fish scales, or shingles on a roof?

Needles flattened as if ironed = *Arbor Vitae* (*White Cedar*)

Needles prickly as well as scale-like = *Red Cedar*

4. If it has *leaves*, are they *opposite* each other, or *alternate?*

Often the branches will grow the same way.

5. Are the leaves *simple* or *compound?*

Look for a bud where the leaf or leaflet joins the stem. Only the true leaf, not the leaflet, will have one formed there.

6. Has the leaf *one main vein* or *more than one?*

An oak leaf, for instance, has *one,* but a maple leaf has *three* or *five*.

7. Is the outline of the leaf *even* or *uneven?*

Fold the leaf in half from top to bottom, and see whether the sides are *equal* and the edges matching. (Are the teeth regular or irregular?)

When you have asked these questions about trees with *leaves,* you will not have the exact answer, but you'll find that you know enough about the species to be able to look it up in almost any tree guide. Especially useful for this purpose is the *Tree Finder,* published by the Nature Study Guild in Naperville, Illinois. This little book is a great bargain and should be in everyone's pocket.

Evergreens for Christmas. Did you know that the idea of evergreens in our homes each December began long before the first Christmas? As you've noticed, the shortest days of the year come around the 21st, the time of the winter solstice. Once long ago the people on earth feared that the gods might continue to make the days shorter and shorter until there was no daylight left at all. So they brought into their houses, or caves, evergreen boughs, symbols of life to them, unchanging and lasting. And when they noticed that the days were growing longer again, they believed the greens had protected them from eternal darkness, and had pleased the gods. Every year thereafter, as the hours of light grew shortest, these early inhabitants of the world brought in their evergreens, and sure enough, the days began to lengthen.

We bring in greens for different reasons now. And we add the Christmas tree for a holy birth, the holly berry for its color, and the mistletoe for its "magic powers." But along with these let's also remember to bring some of the oldest greens of all, the ground cedar and the running pine that were here when the earth was young, so that once a year at least we may think of the people of so long ago who worshipped many gods and lived in dread of an endless night.

Leaf Suggestions. Why not make a leaf collection, either of pressed leaves or leaf prints? Both of these are good ways to learn the leaves, and good records to have of the trees that you know. And they're decorative too. Leaf skeletons are much prettier than they sound. Most hobby and nature activity books (see last section of *Notes*) tell how leaf collections, prints, and "skeletons" are made. *Note:* Try making some leaf-print Christmas cards.

Read about the Trees.

A Pocket Guide to the Trees. Rutherford Platt. Pocket Books, Inc., New York.

American Trees. Rutherford Platt. Dodd, Mead & Company, New York.

An Introduction to Trees. John Kieran. Hanover House, Garden City, New York.

Life of the Forest Floor. William Hopkins Amos. Nelson Doubleday, Inc. and National Audubon Society, New York.

Natural History of the Trees. Donald Culross Peattie. Houghton Mifflin Company, Boston.

Our American Trees. Ruth H. Dudley. Thomas Y. Crowell Company, New York.

See Through the Forest. Millicent Selsam. Harper & Brothers, New York.

The Woods of Time. Rutherford Platt. Dodd, Mead & Company, New York.

This Green World. Rutherford Platt. Dodd, Mead & Company, New York.

Tree Neighbors. Russell Doubleday. Doubleday & Company, Inc., Garden City, New York.

Trees. Herbert S. Zim and Alexander C. Martin. Simon and Schuster, Inc., New York.

Trees and Their Story. Dorothy Sterling. Doubleday & Company, Inc., Garden City, New York.

Trees and Trails. Clarence J. Hylander. The Macmillan Company, New York.

Trees of the Eastern and Central United States and Canada. William H. Harlow. Dover Publications, Inc., New York.

A pond is a world of its own, a complete community. It is also a nature museum, where you can visit at any time, stay as long as you like, pay no admission, and often bring specimens home for further observation and enjoyment.

Here are a few pond projects:

Make a Waterscope. With one of these you can look beneath the surface and see the underwater life. And they are not difficult to make. Begin with a clear glass jar. To the top of it (the rim) attach with heavy tape a cardboard cylinder (the kind that is used for mailing calendars). Hold the scope so that the bottom of the jar is just below the surface, taking care not to wet the cardboard. Now peer through the top of the cylinder.

A wooden bucket with a glass window pane inserted in the bottom makes an even better waterscope if the bucket and glass are available.

A pyrex baking dish, if it's deep enough, will always do if you're in a hurry.

Make a Dipnet. Almost anything can serve as a dipnet—a kitchen strainer, a stocking with a wire loop around the open end to hold it out, or any strong but finely meshed net tied at one end and attached at the other to a hoop on the end of a pole. If the circular frame of the hoop is flattened on the edge away from the handle, it becomes quite easy to scrape the bottom.

A very professional-looking bottom scraper may be made from an ordinary window screen to which six-inch wooden sides have been fastened to form an open "box." One side should lean out at a 45° angle for easier scraping.

Examine your catch in shallow white enamel pans, or baking dishes painted white. The light-colored background helps you to see better what you have caught. Take your specimens home, with plenty of pond water, in large glass jars that have screen tops if possible, otherwise holes punched in the lids.

Make an Aquarium. You will want to keep the pond life you have brought home where it will thrive, and where you can look at it often. If you make an aquarium you will probably become so intrigued by all that is going on inside that you will spend a great deal of time just sitting in front of it, watching.

Select a straight-sided glass tank with enough room to accommodate all the material you have brought. It will be a temptation to overcrowd the aquarium, since you will be anxious to get everything in. In this case it is better to have two tanks or even more. Pond life is accustomed to plenty

145

of space, and needs it. Tanks may be made at home (see nature hobby books) or bought at most pet shops.

Place the aquarium where it will have indirect light (east or north window) rather than full sun all day, and where the temperature remains between 60° and 70°.

Now you are ready to fill the aquarium. Begin with a layer of *well-washed* sand, varying in depth from 2″ at one end of the tank to 1″ at the other. Then carefully pour in clear, strained pond water or rain water. To avoid stirring up the sand, the water should be run slowly first into a tilted saucer in one corner of the tank, or against a spoon or the side of the aquarium. A piece of heavy paper may be laid over the sand during the pouring and removed later. Fill the tank about half full.

Next comes the planting, before any animals go in. Plants are not only a most attractive addition, but also, by giving off oxygen, help maintain the balance of the aquarium. Use the small plants that grow on the floor of your pond. Push the roots into the sand, or tie them to little stones buried in it. Be sure not to overplant; you want to be able to see the rest of the pond life. Then, still carefully, pour in the rest of the water until it comes to within an inch of the top of the tank.

Now wait and give the aquarium a few days to establish itself. The water will clear, and the plants become adjusted to their move. After that you can add the animals you have brought. Actually it is a good idea to get the aquarium ready *first*, and then go find the animals. Remember to include some pond snails; they help keep the tank clean.

From time to time, to maintain the water level, pond or rain water at room temperature should be added. A piece of window glass may be placed over the tank, but have it slightly raised so that air may still circulate. A screen across the top of the tank will collect any insects rising from the water.

When it comes to feeding, native food is always preferable (pond skimmings, chopped earthworms, etc.). But there may be times when you will have to use shredded lettuce, raw ground meat, cooked egg yolk, or some commercial product recommended by a pet shop. This depends, of course, on what you have in your aquarium. It is important to know the food needs of each inhabitant. *Do* refer to one of the books on the subject mentioned further on in the *Notes*. Put a little food on the surface of the water to see if the animals are hungry. If they do not accept one kind, try another. But be careful not to overfeed them. And do not leave uneaten food too long. If it has fallen to the bottom it can be removed with a pipette.

Tragedy in the tank! Sometimes even in the best-ordered aquariums you

146

may find that one animal will prey upon another. The only thing you can do is separate these species *next* time, using a second aquarium, or return the predator to the pond.

Note: when returning an animal to the out-of-doors, be sure to take it back to the place, or kind of place, where you found it. And on your pond trips remember to wear wading boots or old sneakers that you don't mind getting wet and muddy.

Make a Tracking Expedition around the Pond. Pond edges, of mud or damp sand, are just the places to look for the tracks of animals that have come to the water to drink or to fish. Here the prints of muskrat, raccoon, possum, fox, deer, beaver, great blue heron, bittern, spotted and solitary sandpipers, and many more may be found. A woodcock will often leave its mark in such a place, little round holes where its long bill has probed for food. Make a list and discover how many unseen visitors enjoy your pond with you.

To help you identify the tracks you find, you will want to consult at least one book on the subject. There are several.

A Field Guide to Animal Tracks. Olaus Murie. Houghton Mifflin Company, Boston.

Animal Tracks. George F. Mason. William Morrow & Company, New York.

Animal Tracks. Introduction by H. Marlin Perkins. The Stackpole Company, Harrisburg, Pennsylvania.

Tracks and Trailcraft. Ellsworth Jaeger. The Macmillan Company, New York.

Who Went There? Carroll Colby. Aladdin Books, New York.

Track Casts are Fun to Have. You might like to start your own nature museum at home. A shelf of impressions of animal tracks, neatly labeled, would be of great interest. Detailed instructions for making these casts are included in many hobby and natural history books. Some especially good suggestions may be found in William Hillcourt's *Field Book of Nature Activities* (G. P. Putnam's Sons, New York), pp. 132-36.

Read a Book on Pond Life. There are some good ones.

Beginner's Guide to Fresh Water Life. Leon A. Hausman. G. P. Putnam's Sons, New York.

Field Book of Ponds and Streams. Ann H. Morgan. G. P. Putnam's Sons, New York.

In Ponds and Streams. Margaret Waring Buck. Abingdon Press, New York.

Life in a Woodland Pond. Charles E. Mohr. Nelson Doubleday, Inc. and National Audubon Society, New York.

Pond Life. Jean Garvett and Paxton Chadwick. Penguin Books, Baltimore.

INSECT INTERESTS

In his *Field Book of Insects* (G. P. Putnam's Sons, New York) Dr. Frank E. Lutz suggests that anyone interested in insects should have good eyes, nimble fingers, and an inquiring mind. To these I should add strong legs and patience. It's safe to assume, I'm sure, that any young naturalist has *most* of these qualifications.

Here are a few more things you may want or need:

An Insect Net. A nature hobby book will tell you how to make one. Good nets may also be purchased quite inexpensively.

A Hand Lens or Magnifier. You will find many uses for this besides examining insects, and should have one with you wherever you go.

An Ant Farm or Observation Bee Hive. How thrilling to be able to watch the ants and bees as they go about their highly organized social, domestic, and political lives! You will never tire of watching them, for there is always something happening in their communities, and their industry and ways of living together are truly marvelous to behold. For further information about how you can acquire and maintain one of these projects, write to the General Biological Supply House, Chicago 37, Illinois.

Note: Johnny Appleseed's store in Beverly, Massachusetts, lists a reasonably priced ant farm for sale in a recent catalogue.

A Butterfly Garden. Did you know that you can plant a garden for flower-haunting butterflies, to attract them and bring them around you? And one of the best things about this kind of garden is that the plants butterflies like, because of their fragrance and bright colors, are plants you will like too. Perhaps you already have some of them in your flower borders.

Here are a few suggestions for a butterfly garden:

Shrubs and vines: spicebush, butterfly bush, barberry, lilac, wisteria, and honeysuckle.

Flowers: bee balm, marigold, spider flower, violets, nasturtium, lupine, hollyhock, yucca, heliotrope, iris, zinnia, verbena, and those with long narrow tubes, or spurs: nicotiana, phlox, and columbine.

Such wildflowers as asters, clovers, dogbane, milkweeds, thistles, and some of the grasses that you might not want in your flower beds could be planted nearby.

Note: Cut-out butterfly "decoys" pinned to blossoms will sometimes attract their real-life counterparts.

In his *Field Guide to the Butterflies* (Houghton Mifflin Company, Boston) Alexander B. Klots includes a list of the larval food plants of butterflies. This should be helpful to you in deciding what to plant, as well as in looking for butterflies and their larvae. It is very useful, when hunting for insects, to know by name and sight the particular plants they prefer, where they are most apt to be found.

To Start an Insect Collection. When you feel that you are ready to begin an insect collection of your own, you will need, besides your net and a field guide, a killing jar, a spreading board, insect pins, and display cases. Some of these you can make yourself. Others should be obtained from scientific supply houses. Many (such as Ward's Natural Science Establishment, 3000 Ridge Road East, Rochester 9, New York) have catalogues which they will send on request. For those of you who wish to specialize in moths and butterflies, there is the Butterfly Collection Supply House, 639 Walnut Street, Irwin, Pennsylvania.

Field guides usually give instructions for collecting, mounting, and preserving insects. *Do* use labels and notes. A specimen, no matter how beautiful, is of no scientific value unless you know what it is and where and when it was caught. Mount your insects as soon after killing as possible. If they lie around they will get ragged-looking and broken, and not worth keeping. And you will have wastefully destroyed a living thing.

To Band a Monarch. Would you like to join Dr. F. A. Urquhart in his project of banding migratory monarch butterflies? A letter to him at the Royal Ontario Museum, Toronto 5, Ontario, Canada, stating your qualifications, would be a good way to begin. Miss Ivy LeMon, at Drumlin Farm in South Lincoln, Massachusetts, would also be glad to tell you about this exciting program. What fun to be a butterfly bander!

And if you should catch a banded monarch in your net, be sure to: 1. Copy down the number on the band, but don't remove the band, 2. Send to the Royal Museum the number and also the time and place you caught the butterfly, and 3. Let the monarch go safely on its way as soon as possible, so somebody else, perhaps hundreds of miles from you, may also record it.

To Read About Insects. You may pick and choose. There seem to be nearly as many insect books as there are insects themselves! Besides the two field guides already mentioned, here are some more:

All About Moths and Butterflies. Robert S. Lemmon. Random House, Inc., New York.

All About the Insect World. Ferdinand C. Lane. Random House, Inc., New York.

An Introduction to the Study of Insects. Donald J. Borror and Dwight M. DeLong. Rinehart & Company, Inc., New York.

Butterfly Chrysalids. Richard Headstrom. Natural History Museum, Worcester, Massachusetts.

City of the Bees. Frank S. Stuart. McGraw-Hill Book Company, New York.

Collecting Cocoons. Lois J. Hussey and Catherine Pessino. Thomas Y. Crowell Company, New York.

Fabre's Book of Insects. Dodd, Mead & Company, New York.

Grassroot Jungles. Edwin Way Teale. Dodd, Mead & Company, New York.

How to Know the Insects. H. E. Jaques. William C. Browne Company, Dubuque, Iowa.

Insect Engineers. Ruth Bartlett. Morrow Junior Books, William Morrow & Company, New York.

Insects. Herbert S. Zim and Clarence Cottam. Simon and Schuster, New York.

Insects in Their World. Su Zan N. Swain. Garden City Books, Garden City, New York.

Insects on Parade. Clarence J. Hylander. The Macmillan Company, New York.

The Ant World. Derek W. Morley. Penguin Books, Baltimore.

The Grasshopper Book. Wilfred S. Bronson. Harcourt, Brace & Company, New York.

The Insect Guide. Ralph Swain. Doubleday & Company, New York.

The Junior Book of Insects. Edwin Way Teale. E. P. Dutton & Company, Inc., New York.

The Life of the Bee. Maurice Maeterlinck. New American Library, New York.

The Wonder Book of Ants. Wilfred S. Bronson. Harcourt, Brace & Company, New York.

"ANCIENT ANIMALS"

Reptiles and amphibians were among the earliest settlers of the earth. When you see the ones we know today, think of their ancestors and try to imagine some of them—Eryops, Allosaurus, and Trachadon. Look up their pictures and go to see their models and their bones in museums. You'll be fascinated.

You'll be fascinated too with their descendants, the snakes, lizards, and turtles; the frogs, toads, and salamanders, of the present. They are not difficult to see, once you begin keeping an eye out for them. And you might even want to bring one home for a pet.

Note: Alligators and crocodiles are also reptiles, and perhaps resemble most closely old Eryops. Their range, however, is limited to a very small part of this country.

Some Suggestions for Finding Reptiles and Amphibians. SNAKES. Look for these on sunny days from spring to fall. Sometimes in summer they can be found at night too. Good places to look are in deserted burrows; on rock ledges if the day is bright and cool; on branches and logs; along roadsides; in rotting stumps and piles of leaves; in fields where there are cornstalks; in barns; under stones and debris; in swamps and wooded areas; and in ponds and streams (for water snakes).

Note: Snakes can't hear you coming, but they may catch the vibrations of your movements, so step with care. LIZARDS. The greatest variety can be found in the south and southwest. Look on sandy deserts, in dry rock walls, or under rotten stumps and logs. *Note:* Lizards are very numerous in the tropics, scurrying in plain sight about people's courtyards and balconies. TURTLES. When they are nesting is a good time to look for them. Also search around lakes and streams, where they may be sunning on logs; in ponds, in damp or brushy fields, and woods; and watch for them crossing roads. They like to feel the warmth of the pavement.

SALAMANDERS. These are often found after a rain. Some species are nocturnal. Look in running brooks and shallow pools; in woodlands; in meadows near marshes; in old stumps; under logs and rocks; in leafy ravines; in nearly dried-up stream beds; and in shady caves. FROGS. At night in spring go to a pond or marsh with a flashlight. A drizzly night is said to be best, but almost any evening when they are breeding, if you wade into the water a little way, you can catch them in your flashlight beam, and sometimes in your hand. TOADS. You should find them in your garden and even on your lawn, in the loose soil of cultivated land, and occasionally in open woodlands. *Hint:* Do not remove toads from your garden. They are worth their weight in gold there. *Note:* Naturally you will not find all kinds in all places. These suggestions are made to give you an idea where to start looking. You will discover many other good locations to add to this list.

Wild Pets. Some reptiles and amphibians make interesting, entertaining, and rewarding pets. Many are easy to feed and care for, and are relatively long-lived. Others, though, you will not find particularly responsive or companionable. Most will have slow reactions, and some will be quite indifferent to food and unco-operative about eating.

Before you decide on one as a pet, be sure that you know how often and what to feed it, and in what you should house it. There are several excellent books on the subject. *The Book of Wild Pets* by Clifford B. Moore (Charles

151

T. Branford Company, Boston) is a standard. *How to Make a Miniature Zoo* by Vinson Brown (Little, Brown & Company, Boston) and *Home-Made Zoo* by Sylvia S. Greenberg and Edith L. Raskin (David McKay Company, New York) are also good ones. Buy one of these first, and then go out and look for your pet.

Read more about these "ancient animals."
All About Strange Beasts of the Past. Roy Chapman Andrews. Random House, Inc., New York.
Boy's Book of Frogs, Toads, and Salamanders. Percy A. Morris. The Ronald Press Company, New York.
Boy's Book of Snakes. Percy A. Morris. The Ronald Press Company, New York.
Dinosaurs. Herbert S. Zim. Simon and Schuster, Inc., New York.
Field Book of Snakes of the United States and Canada. Karl P. Schmidt and D. Dwight Davis. G. P. Putnam's Sons, New York.
Handbook of Frogs and Toads. Anna A. and Albert H. Wright. Comstock Publishing Associates, Ithaca, New York.
Handbook of Lizards. Hobart M. Smith. Comstock Publishing Associates, Ithaca, New York.
Handbook of Salamanders. Sherman C. Bishop. Comstock Publishing Associates, Ithaca, New York.
Prehistoric Animals. William E. Scheele. World Publishing Company, Cleveland.
Reptiles and Amphibians. Herbert S. Zim and Hobart M. Smith. Simon and Schuster, New York.
Snakes. Herbert S. Zim. William Morrow & Company, New York.
Snakes Alive and How They Live. Clifford H. Pope. The Viking Press, New York.
The Book of Reptiles and Amphibians. Michael H. Bevans. Garden City Books, Garden City, New York.
The Reptiles of North America. Raymond L. Ditmars. Doubleday & Company, Inc., New York.
Turtles of the United States and Canada. Clifford H. Pope. Alfred A. Knopf, Inc., New York.

PLANT PROJECTS

Plants are literally everywhere. They are attractive, abundant, and easy to study and get to know. And besides enjoying them in their natural state, there are many interesting things that you can do with plants. Here are a few ideas:

A Woodland Terrarium. For its own beauty as well as for a home for certain wild pets, a woodland terrarium is well worth having. Begin with an aquarium-like tank if it is to hold animals too. Otherwise any pleasingly-shaped glass container will do. Fish bowls and brandy snifters are often used. Just be sure you have a window pane, or fitted piece of glass, to cover the top. Line the bottom with pebbles and bits of damp moss tucked in the outside edges to show green. A piece of charcoal will help keep the terrarium fresh. Next add a layer of moist leaf mold and more moss, and you are ready to plant.

Go to the woods for your terrarium plants, and look along the forest floor. Partridgeberry (be sure it has its red berries on it), wintergreen, small ferns, rattlesnake plantain (if it is not protected and if you can find it), and low pipsissewa are all desirable. Ground pine and cedar may be used. Bits of wood with British soldier lichen and lichened stones should be included. And you will be surprised to see what you have planted that you did not know about. Unexpected starflowers, wild lilies of the valley, and wood violets as well may start up during the winter.

For a *bog terrarium,* or dish garden, to hold specimens from your bog trip, begin with a layer of washed gravel, then one of wet sphagnum moss and bog soil. Plant your sundews, bladderworts, and small pitcher plants as deep as they grew where you collected them. Water both terraria with a very fine spray.

A Wildflower Garden. This is not as easy as it sounds. It's natural to assume that if a plant does well in the wild, it will do even better under cultivation. But this is usually far from true. Wildflowers do well where they are growing because they have become adapted to their particular surroundings. The best way to insure safe transplanting is to bring back with the plant as much as you can carry of its native soil. Then set it in a spot where, as nearly as possible, there are the same conditions of moisture, earth, and light and shade.

Here are a few more hints that may help you in wildflower gardening:
1. First know which plants are protected in your state, and leave these where they are growing.* 2. If you are on someone else's property, ask permission to dig up plants. 3. Take only a few of one kind at a time until you see if they will survive in your garden. 4. On the other hand, don't plant a hodge-podge of different flowers. This is not "natural." 5. Don't let the plant know it is being moved; that is, work quickly, but carefully. 6. Some wildflowers stand being transplanted more readily than others. Write

-----

* In any case, remember that you are a conservationist. A good rule to follow for *un*protected plants is, "If there are five, leave them to thrive; If there are ten, take one then."

to the Wild Flower Preservation Society, Washington, D.C., for the recommended ones for your area. They will also send you a list of those that are protected. 7. *Growing Woodland Plants* by Clarence and Eleanor Birdseye (Oxford University Press, Inc., New York) and *Wildflowers and How to Grow Them* by Edwin F. Steffek (Crown Publishers Inc., New York) contain much useful information.

A Fern Corner. Devote one corner of your wildflower garden to ferns. A semi-shaded rocky slope is ideal for this. You may have to experiment to see which kind will flourish there. Observe carefully the natural surroundings of each fern that you move, and try to imitate these in your garden. Look up the ferns in a field guide and label your specimens. Your fern corner might well become a centre of attraction. It would be a good place for a birdbath, perhaps a natural one hollowed out of rough rock, or a graceful lead shell.

Note: For more ideas see *Wild Flowers and Ferns in Their Homes and in Our Gardens* by Herbert Durand (G. P. Putnam's Sons, New York).

Plant Books. These are only a few of many.

A Field Guide to the Ferns. Boughton Cobb. Houghton Mifflin Company, Boston.

All About the Flowering World. Ferdinand C. Lane. Random House, Inc., New York.

American Wild Flowers. Harold H. Moldenke. D. Van Nostrand Company, Inc., New York.

An Introduction to Wildflowers. John Kieran. Garden City Books, Garden City, New York.

Beginner's Guide to Wild Flowers. Ethel Hinkley Hausman. G. P. Putnam's Sons, New York.

Ferns. Farida A. Wiley. American Museum of Natural History, New York.

Field Book of American Wild Flowers. F. Schuyler Mathews. G. P. Putnam's Sons, New York.

Flowers. Herbert S. Zim and Alexander C. Martin. Simon and Schuster, Inc., New York.

How to Know the Mosses. Henry S. Conrad. William D. Browne Company, Dubuque, Iowa.

How to Know the Wildflowers. Alfred Stefferud. New American Library, New York.

Mushrooms of Eastern Canada and the United States. R. Pomerleau. Chanticleer, Ltd., Montreal.

Native Ferns. Virginia Eifert. Canadian Nature Magazine, Toronto.

Our Flowering World. Rutherford Platt. Dodd, Mead & Company, New York.

The Book of Wild Flowers for Young People. F. Schuyler Mathews, G. P. Putnam's Sons, New York.

The Pocket Guide to the Wildflowers. Samuel Gottscho. Pocket Books, Inc., New York.

The Story of Mosses, Ferns, and Mushrooms. Dorothy Sterling. Doubleday & Company, Inc., Garden City, New York.

Using Wayside Plants. Nelson Coon. Watertown, Massachusetts.

Wild Flower Guide. Edgar T. Wherry. Doubleday & Company, Inc., New York.

IT'S FUN TO BE A STAR-GAZER

For star-gazing you need no more equipment than your own eyes. Anyone with good eyesight may see as many as 2000 stars on a cloudless, moonless night. With field glasses even more can be seen. And a telescope, of course, opens up whole new vistas in the heavens. If you become really interested in astronomy, you might want to make or buy a small telescope of your own.

Begin your star-gazing with the bright stars. The brightest, Sirius, is visible to us only in winter. The nearest star (excluding the sun) is not our brightest, as one might think. It is, in fact, so faint that it can be seen only with a telescope. Yet it is not quite four and a half light-years away! Sirius is almost nine light-years from the earth. Antares, which is bright and red and easy to see, is actually a very distant star. We can assume then that it is tremendous; it has, in fact, been said to have a diameter four hundred times that of our sun.

Some stars are much hotter than others, and the hottest, strangely enough, are not red, but bluish-white. Vega is one of these. Red Antares has a comparatively low temperature.

The familiar bright stars and their constellations ° are (in order of brightness):

Sirius	in Canis Major (the Great Dog)
Vega	in Lyra (the Lyre)
Capella	in Auriga (the Charioteer)
Arcturus	in Boötes (the Herdsman)

° *Constellation* means literally "stars together." It's fun to know them and be able to recognize them again as the year goes by, for each season has its different constellations overhead. Most star books have sky maps for spring, summer, fall, and winter. If you use a sky chart out-of-doors, cover your flashlight with thin, dark paper so that the rays will not detract from the light of the stars.

Rigel	in Orion (the Hunter)
Procyon	in Canis Minor (the Little Dog)
Altair	in Aquila (the Eagle)
Betelgeuse	in Orion (the Hunter)
Aldebaran	in Taurus (the Bull)
Pollux	in Gemini (the Twins)
Spica	in Virgo (the Virgin)
Antares	in Scorpius (the Scorpion)
Fomalhaut	in Pisces Australis (the Southern Fish)
Deneb	in Cygnus (the Swan)
Regulus	in Leo (the Lion)
Castor	in Gemini (the Twins)

Zodiac means "circle of animals." Once all twelve of the signs were named for animals. From earliest times people have believed that the stars held a clue to their destinies, and they have tried to tell their fortunes by them. Even today there are those who think that somebody born under the sign of Aquarius has one definite set of traits or qualities, while another born under Leo or Taurus has an entirely different character. To be born under a sign means that on the day of one's birth the sun appeared rising and setting in a certain constellation. These constellations reach around the earth in a belt, or path, down which the sun and moon and all the planets seem to move.

Here's an old verse to help you remember the order of the "circle of animals:"

> The Ram, the Bull, the Heavenly Twins,
> And next the Crab, the Lion shines,
> The Virgin, and the Scales,
> The Scorpion, Archer, and Sea Goat,
> The Man that bears the Watering Pot,
> The Fish with shining Tails.

Shooting Stars, or meteors,* can be seen on almost any clear night. While most are observed after midnight, you can, if you are lucky, sometimes spot five to ten before bedtime. In "star showers" as many as one hundred an hour have been recorded. Keep count of the number you see on an ordinary evening, and then the amount you see during a "shower." Notice how they vary in size, brilliance, and speed.

---

* A meteor*ite* is a meteor, or fragment of meteor, that happens to reach the earth's surface. These are very interesting to see. Most natural history museums have one or more.

For an evening of counting meteors, find yourself a good place for seeing as much of the sky as possible, away from lights, tall trees, and buildings. Use a deck chair, or lie flat on an air mattress. Be sure to have warm clothes and a blanket, even in summer. And it's also a good idea to have some insect repellent handy.

Here are the dates and parts of the sky where the best star showers occur:

January	1- 4	the Quadrantids	East, between Boötes and Draco
April	19-23	the Lyrids	Northeast, between Vega and Hercules
May	1- 6	the May Aquarids	East, southwest of Pegasus
August	10-14	the Perseids	Northeast, from Perseus
October	18-23	the Orionids	East, between Orion and Gemini
November	14-18	the Leonids	Northeast, from Leo
December	10-13	the Geminids	East, near Castor in Gemini

Planets are worthwhile to know too, because they often appear so brightly in the dusk or dawn. Then they are called evening, or morning, stars. They are not stars, of course, but bodies which, like the moon, give off no glow of their own making but reflect the light of the sun. The word planet means "wanderer."

Since they do wander, they cannot be shown on the star maps in books. But in many newspapers, on the first day of each month, you will find a sky chart for that month showing the positions of the visible planets. Sometimes three or four, or even as many as five, evening stars may be lined up in the west. Such a parade of planets is truly wonderful to see.

Star Tracks. On a clear, moonless night, if you set your camera out-of-doors pointing to the sky, and leave the shutter open for several hours, you will find when the film is developed a series of thin, white lines, the tracks the stars have made across the sky. Be sure to tell your developer to print all of your pictures. Otherwise he might think your star tracks were a mistake, a picture of nothing!

Visit museums for their model exhibits, planetariums for their variety of sky programs, and observatories, when they are open to the public, for the chance to look through a great telescope. You will never forget such experiences.

A Star Finder, which shows the principal stars visible at every hour of the year, is an excellent guide to the heavens. C. S. Hammond & Company, Inc., Maplewood, New Jersey, makes a splendid one. It is light to carry, easy to use, and the best way I know to learn and locate the stars.

Star Books are plentiful, and vary in scope and approach. Look them over, if it's possible, before you buy. Here are some good ones:

157

A Beginner's Star Book. Kelvin McKready. G. P. Putnam's Sons, New York.

A Dipper Full of Stars. Lou Williams. Wilcox & Follett Company, Chicago.

A Field Book of the Skies. William T. Olcott and Edmund W. Putnam. G. P. Putnam's Sons, New York.

A Field Book of the Stars. William T. Olcott. G. P. Putnam's Sons, New York.

All About the Stars. Anne T. White. Random House, Inc., New York.

Find the Constellations. H. A. Rey. Houghton Mifflin Company, Boston.

Introducing the Constellations. Robert H. Baker. The Viking Press, New York.

Stars. Herbert S. Zim and Robert H. Baker. Simon and Schuster, Inc., New York.

The Stars. H. A. Rey. Houghton Mifflin Company, Boston.

The Stars for Sam. W. M. Reed. Harcourt, Brace & Company, New York.

This Way to the Stars. John M. Schealer. E. P. Dutton & Company, Inc., New York.

What's in the Sky? Miriam Phillips Dunham. Oxford University Press, Inc., New York.

When the Stars Come Out. Robert H. Baker. The Viking Press, New York.

And you might also want *The Luminous Pocket Planetarium.* National Boy Scout Supply Service, New York.

ALONG THE NATURE TRAIL

After you have laid out your trail (a ball of twine going from tree to tree will keep you from getting lost and show you where to cut), and made it wide enough to walk on (single file), you are ready for the markers.

The best ones are made of wood or metal. *Wooden markers* may be screwed to rustic posts, or fastened to trees. Hinged ones, with a flap that lifts up to reveal the label, are practical and popular. The wood may be painted before lettering, if you like. Stained wood looks more natural though.

Metal markers can be cut from sheets of tin, aluminum, or zinc with regular tin shears. The pieces should then be buried in the ground for about a week to season and etch the surface. With a nail make a hole in the top of the marker, string wire through it, and tie it to a tree or post.

For *labeling*, use a broad-point lettering pen and India ink. You'll find that if you rub the surface with an eraser first, the ink will go on more easily. Letters should be tall enough so that they can be read without having to stoop down.

The *wording* is really up to you. Some nature trails are marked simply with the names of the objects of interest. Others have labels that tell something about the object, and give some hint or clue for recognizing it the next time. These are especially valuable. But your own ideas are valuable too. Don't be afraid to be original. You might want to indicate on the marker *why* you chose that particular tree, or shrub, or rock. People like to know things like that.

Some good references:
Nature Trails. Roger Tory Peterson. National Audubon Society, New York.
Ten Years of Nature Trails and *Trailside Action.* William H. Carr. American Museum of Natural History, New York.
Almost any nature activity book.

The Trail Continues

"Life is life's greatest richness," a wise naturalist once said. And it's all around us, wherever we look. Every day that we walk in the open, or anywhere under the sky, we are taking a step forward along the nature trail. Every project we complete, in the field or at home; every book we read; every friend we interest; and every glimpse and idea we have that helps us understand natural history and conservation leads us still farther down the path. Where does it end? I say it never ends, that it goes on and on. And I hope you will think so too, and want to stay on it all your life.

Some Nature and Nature Hobby Books:
The Amateur Naturalist's Handbook. Vinson Brown. Little, Brown & Company, Boston.
Field Book of Nature Activities. William Hillcourt. G. P. Putnam's Sons, New York.
How to Make a Home Nature Museum. Vinson Brown. Little, Brown & Company, Boston.
The Book of Nature Hobbies. Ted Pettit. Didier Publishing Company, New York.
Adventuring in Nature. Betty Price. National Recreation Association, New York.
Partners with Nature. Ivah Green. International Textbook Company, Scranton, Pennsylvania.
Discovering Nature the Year Round. Anne Marie Jauss. Aladdin Books, New York.
Nature Notebook. Robert Candy. Houghton Mifflin Company, Boston.

The Golden Treasury of Natural History. Bertha Morris Parker. Simon and Schuster, Inc., New York.

The World We Live In. Editorial staff of LIFE. Simon and Schuster, Inc., New York.

Out of Doors in Summer. Clarence J. Hylander. The Macmillan Company, New York.

Seven Suggestions for Further Nature Activities.

1. *Join your local Audubon Society or Bird Club.* Youth members are most welcome. You'll enjoy going on field trips with "experts," and you'll find they are interested in *many* phases of natural history. If there is no such group near you, see if there is anything you can do to get one started.

2. *Join an Audubon Junior Club.* All over the world boys and girls are discovering more and more about the out-of-doors through these club projects. Write to the National Audubon Society, 1130 Fifth Avenue, New York 28, New York.

3. *Attend Camp Wildwood.* Boys and girls from nine to fourteen are eligible. David R. Miner, Wildwood Nature Camp, Barre, Massachusetts, will be glad to send you a folder.

4. *Go to a Nature Day Camp.* Did you know that there may be one quite near you? Ask your science teacher.

5. *Subscribe to a Nature Magazine.* AUDUBON MAGAZINE (National Audubon Society), JUNIOR NATURAL HISTORY (American Museum of Natural History), and NATURE MAGAZINE (American Nature Association, Washington, D.C.) are good ones.

6. *Visit a Natural History Museum.* And go often, because they change the displays from time to time, and even if they did not there would be more than you could see in a day, or in a week or month at some museums. Ask about lectures. Sometimes they have Explorers' Clubs, and the kind of nature courses you may have been wishing for.

7. *Use your Public Libraries.* You'll be amazed at the number of books on every subject, and for every age. You might go to read up on just your own particular hobby, and come home with an entirely new interest. Don't hesitate to ask for assistance. Librarians know about books and like to discuss them. Ask questions, and soon you'll be *answering* questions, and sharing what *you* know too.